THE CHRISTIAN STAKE IN SCIENCE

THE CHRISTIAN STAKE
IN SCIENCE

by

ROBERT E. D. CLARK, M.A., Ph.D.

9621

MOODY PRESS • CHICAGO

MOODY PRESS EDITION 1967

Published by special arrangement with
THE PATERNOSTER PRESS, EXETER, DEVON, ENGLAND

Printed in the United States of America

CONTENTS

Parts of Chapters 3, 5 and 6 of this book were broadcast over the B.B.C's Eastern German programme, and parts of Chapters 2, 8 and 17 have appeared in *Faith and Thought*, published by the Victoria Institute, to whom also a lecture was given containing the substance of the material of Chapters 11 to 13.

WHAT THIS BOOK IS ABOUT

IN THE NINETEENTH CENTURY IT SEEMED TO MANY PEOPLE
that science was rapidly destroying religious belief. The stage
had long been set. A few generations earlier it had been decided
that the earth could no longer be regarded as the centre of the
universe. Later came the discovery of inexorable scientific laws
which seemed to make belief in the Christian miracles untenable.
Now, in the Victorian age, science was fast winning all along the
line. The margin of the Authorized Version of the Bible declared
that God had created the earth in 4004 B.C., but now science was
beginning to measure its age in millions of years; it had been
supposed that the main features of geology could best be understood in terms of the catastrophe of the Noachian deluge, but
geologists were finding new and better explanations; the Church
had taught that there had been neither death nor suffering in the
animal world before the fall of man, but fossils were beginning to
show that creatures had lived and died long before the days of
Adam and Eve, and that parasites existed then as they do today.
Most disturbing of all, religion had taught that man was a special
creation, but now scientists were saying that he had descended
from an ape.

A hangover from these old controversies remains with us today.
Though scientists and theologians no longer do battle about the
old issues, these are by no means forgotten. Atheists still think that
science, having won her battles, has no need to fight them a second
time: Christians still read the stories of the old disputes and hope
to learn from past mistakes.

A common Christian argument runs like this: Victorian Christians were exceedingly foolish to get their science and their
religion mixed up in the way they did—they should have realized
from the start that science and religion deal with separate spheres
which cannot mix. Today we need to recognize once and for all,
Christianity has no stake in science—all scientific theories are
equally compatible or incompatible with Christianity. Science and

religion are simply different, that is all: they can neither conflict with nor support each other.

But many think this is going too far. Two dogs, confined to their kennels, they say, cannot fight, but this is not because their species are so diverse that fighting is impossible! Assign your religion and your science to different compartments in your mind —and of course they will not interact. But if you do that, how will you ever know if they are capable of agreeing or disagreeing?

There are still some, too, who accept the Victorian idea that science is contrary to faith; and yet others who say that science supports religion in general, but not religion with frills of dogma attached.

And so the debate continues. But the arguments used in support of the views put forward today are still, by and large, coloured by the Victorian era. Few look to see whether the science of today would lead a fairminded man to the same conclusions that he might reach from a study of the nineteenth century controversies. *That* is the purpose of this book.

But how shall we set about the task?

Everyone who thinks will realize that, willy nilly, religious and philosophical opinions *must* have their repercussions upon how we think our world is made, which is also the province of science. In the last resort one cannot be an atheist, agnostic, Christian, Hindu, Buddhist or what not, without entertaining at least *some* ideas about how we think scientific discovery will develop—even if our anticipations are purely negative.

This self-evident fact suggests a simple way by which we may examine the present relations between science and religion. We shall scrutinize some of the instances in which, so to speak, the agnostic and the atheist, on the one hand, and the Christian, on the other, have backed their respective horses in the field of science. We shall look in on the races to see which horses are winning.

CHAPTER I

THREE CHRISTIAN ATTITUDES TO SCIENCE

MANY OF THE EARLY IDEAS OF SCIENCE MAKE US smile today. One of them, which seems unusually odd—though it is easy to understand why it came to be held so readily—was the notion that when a complex structure is devoured by flame, it is not really destroyed. All that happens is that it retreats into an invisible form: but it is ever ready to take shape again if conditions are right.

. . . FROM A ROSE'S ASHES

In the seventeenth century, and even much later, we encounter this idea again and again. It was pressed into service, in particular, to account both for crystallization and for the generation of life in unsterilized fluids.

Until very recently vinegar was made from wine—and the wine, of course, came from grapes. Early scientists neutralized vinegar and on evaporation obtained crystals. Examining them carefully they thought they could see small vines. In the crystallization of the solution they supposed they were witnessing the resurrection of the plants.

Sir Kenelm Digby, Court Physician to Queen Elizabeth I, has left us detailed descriptions of his experiments along the same lines. In one of these he describes how he burnt some nettles and, having mixed the ashes with water and filtered the solution, he put the clear liquid or *lye* as it was then called, on the window-sill where it no doubt evaporated in part. But the weather was cold and before long "the frost congealed it":

"And it is most true, that when the water was congealed into ice, there appeared to be abundance of Nettles frozen in the ice. They did not have the colour of Nettles. No greenness accompanied them. They were white. But otherwise it was impossible for any painter to delineate a throng of Nettles more exactly than they were designed in the water. As soon as the water melted all these ideal shapes vanished; but as soon as it was congealed again, they presently appeared afresh . . . This game I had several times with them."[1]

Digby also claimed to have performed a similar experiment with crayfish which he thought he was able to bring to life again after they had been cremated![2]

At one time a gruesome story was circulated about a malefactor who had been resurrected in a similar manner. After the man had been hanged for his misdeeds an experimenter stole some of his bones at the dead of night and, after treating them in the pre-scribed manner, was terrified to see a smaller edition of the criminal grinning at him in a furious rage![3] At one time it was even suggested that Egyptian mummies might be raised in the same way![4]

The seventeenth-century poet Samuel Butler had these ideas in mind when he wrote:

> If chemists from a rose's ashes
> Can raise the rose itself in glasses.[5]

RESURRECTION

Naturally enough, ideas of this kind proved of interest in a wider context. For many then, as now, the Christian teaching concerning a resurrection at the last day seemed to demand not a mere step but a colossal leap in faith. A fantastic miracle, indeed, that after a man was long dead, he could live again! Was there no way to bring the size of the miracle down to more modest proportions?

This is where the experiments we have thought about came in so handy. We meet the argument, put forward with his usual charm, in Sir Thomas Browne's *Religio Medici* (1642). Browne assumes it

[1] Sir Kenelm Digby, *On the Vegetation of Plants*, 1661, p. 76.
[2] Sir Kenelm Digby, *A Choice Collection of Rare Chymical Secrets and Experiments in Philosophy* . . . , 1682, p. 131 "To Engender Cray-fishes".
[3] C. J. S. Thompson, *The Mystery and Lore of Apparitions*, 1930, p. 287.
[4] F. A. Pouchet, *The Universe* (Eng. ed.), 1870, p. 4.
[5] For further information on this subject see, especially, I. Disraeli, *Curiosities of Literature*, Vol. 3 of 1881 ed., pp. 287 ff.

to be a proven fact that although when a plant has been destroyed by fire, its form seems to have "taken his leave for ever", yet in fact, "such forms are not perished, but withdrawn into their incombustible part, where they lie secure from the action of that devouring element." Since even man, he argues, can revive the plant from its ashes, how foolish it is to imagine that God will have difficulty in raising a man at the last day. In chemical experiments a man may see "in an occular and visible object the types of his resurrection."

Sir Thomas Browne, a responsible and scholarly man, was making the best use he could of the knowledge (or supposed knowledge) of his day. No sign of a two-compartment mind here —his religion and his science are mixing freely! And if the science was wrong—well—who could have known it?

CLERK MAXWELL THINKS DIFFERENTLY

Not all Christians have thought as did Sir Thomas Browne. Quite a different attitude was that of James Clerk Maxwell in the nineteenth century. Maxwell was one of the foremost scientists of his day, indeed of all time. He was also a deeply committed Christian who read his Bible and prayed daily. Like Browne before him, he speculated freely about the religious significance of current discoveries in science. But Maxwell, unlike Browne, guarded his thoughts jealously. There was risk, he said, that if some result of science was used to support or illustrate a theological doctrine, the two would become wedded together in the popular mind. When the science was "dated", then it would seem to all men that religion itself was old-fashioned—married to out-of-date science. This was the reason he gave for declining to join the Victoria Institute which existed (and still exists) to discuss the relations between the Christian faith and current knowledge.[1]

WHAT THEY ARE SAYING TODAY

Today, in the twentieth century, Christian attitudes have changed again. The prevailing mood is that science and religion must be

[1] L. Campbell and W. Garnett, *The Life of James Clerk Maxwell*, 1882, pp. 393, 404. On some occasions, however, Maxwell came out of his shell!

kept well apart. The Christian who is a scientist must pursue his religion and his science separately in full confidence that they are independent disciplines. Thus, speaking of the two cosmological theories at present in vogue, Alan Richardson says: "Christian theology is indifferent as to which of these hypotheses (or neither of them) is correct, because today it is no longer supposed that there is a cosmology revealed in the Bible which may be either proved or disproved by scientific research."[1] Mascall takes a similar but less extreme view.

The modern writer often imagines the plight of the student who has allowed his Christian faith to become wedded to a particular theory in science, when he learns that science itself has abandoned the theory. The moral to be drawn is that of independence. "I can think of no greater disservice that could be done to the Christian religion," writes Mascall, "than to tie it up with . . . scientific views that are merely temporary."[2]

[1] A. Richardson, *The Bible in the Age of Science*, 1961, p. 29.
[2] E. L. Mascall, *Christian Theology and Natural Science*, 1956, p. 166.

CHAPTER 2

HAS CHRISTIANITY A VESTED INTEREST IN SCIENCE?

WHOS IS RIGHT?

SHALL WE, WITH BROWNE, SEIZE UPON SCIENTIFIC FIND-
ings and use them as best we may in support of Christian
beliefs? Shall we, with Maxwell, speculate freely but keep our
thoughts to ourselves? Or shall we, as with many moderns, keep
our science and our religion wholly separate, both in our own
minds and in our conversations with others?

There are dangers in all three approaches. If we follow Browne,
the science may slip from beneath our feet and leave our religion
stranded. Perhaps this did not matter so much in the days when
the scientific band-wagon to which you attached your faith was
likely to remain in service for a century or two—for by then
religion would have had time to adjust. But today, when scientific
progress which in the past might have taken a century is com-
pressed into a year or two, adjustment is more difficult.

Then what of Clerk Maxwell's attitude? A few of those who are
highly endowed might be able to follow his example. But it
requires a high degree of concentration and of purpose to develop
thoughts alone, as part of one's private religious life, with no
thought of publicity. Few of us could aspire to achieve this: for
most of us, if we so much as try, would soon lose the art of doing
in private what we cannot do in public.

So we are left, it seems, with the modern attitude—that of complete independence. This seems logical, for the Bible is not a textbook of science and its object is not to reveal what man can find
out for himself. Does it not follow that both scientists and
Christians should, like good cobblers, stick to their lasts? The
Christian must think of all scientific theories as equally Christian or
non-Christian. He has no stakes in the outcome of scientific
endeavour; far less does his religion enable him to predict the
course of scientific discovery. The scientist, in return, must not

argue that science makes a religious viewpoint more or less probable. He must stick to science and leave philosophical and religious problems to others. He has no stakes in the outcome of theological discussion.

The argument sounds well. But the conclusion is shocking. In an age when the intellectual climate is so largely determined by science, we shall break the lines of communication between Christian and non-Christian if we insist that religion and science are altogether separate disciplines. This is not the way of harmony; it is the way of suicide.

Origen, in ancient times, explored the interconnexions between Hellenistic thought and Christianity and it is said that no single man did more than he for the Christianization of the West. When, in the thirteenth century, the pagan ideas of the ancients were rediscovered, Christianity seemed to be threatened till Aquinas showed that reconciliation was possible. When Christianity loses touch with its surroundings it is in retreat. We cannot, if we are Christians, sit back and say that our religious and our secular thinking are incongruous. If there are no links between them, links must be forged. Men were not created to live with divided minds; we have an inward conviction that things hang together, that truth is one.

But what of the ghost of the haunted lad who, because he had pinned his faith to a scientific theory, found that his religion was endangered when scientists changed their minds? If links are forged, will they not break?

It is just here that we encounter the pathetic fallacy of our time. The links forged in former times may be old and rusty now, a real encumbrance if we treasure them still. But they served their day. They created the sense of oneness of knowledge, and so of all creation, which we lack. If we cannot clean away the rust and apply the polish, we need to find modern equivalents. Perhaps these too will not last for ever, but we need them *now*.

Plainly the conclusion we reached was *wrong*. We must look at our arguments again. When situations of this kind crop up it is often profitable to look for parallel instances, to see if they can throw light on the problem in hand.

CROSS-FERTILIZATION OF IDEAS

The development of science in our day serves to bring a new argument to the fore.

If we insist that science and Christianity should not be brought more closely together, we ought at least to be consistent. If the rule applies here why not elsewhere? There are many disciplines which *seem* unconnected, and if we use the ideas of one of them to illustrate or support a theory in another, then when the ideas in the first change, the second will look old-fashioned.

Thus a biologist, past or present, might argue that it would be foolish to drag the ideas of physics or chemistry into the biological field where they do not properly belong. If this is done, he might say, then when the physicists and chemists change their views, biology will look antiquated. Nor is the example imaginary. For decades after chemists had changed their views about the structure of urea, biologists gave an outworn formula in their textbooks, giving these a decidedly antiquated appearance! Again, many see in the determinism of psychology a harking back to a determinism in physics more in keeping with the nineteenth than the twentieth century.

Ought each science, then, to develop its ideas independently, heedless of what others are thinking in alien fields of thought? This has happened only too often in the past—leaving a bewildering number of contradictions and differences in terminology in the wake. But science is rapidly growing out of this stage. We now realize that advance depends on cross-fertilization of ideas. Most of the great break-throughs in science have come about in this way—especially in biology, which has drawn heavily upon physics, chemistry and mathematics. Insularity is the road to stagnation.

This undoubted fact about the science of our day would seem to suggest that both theology and science might benefit greatly by cross-fertilization.

But the Bible, we say, is not a textbook of science. Of course it is not. But is this a good reason for denying that revelation may *sometimes* give us hints about what we cannot *easily* find out for ourselves? And if it does so, then may we not sometimes find that we have been told beforehand what science can only discover the hard way?

If such a possibility were true, it would solve our difficulties. Science and Christianity would be brought much more closely together, but we might be able to avoid some of the pitfalls which this union would otherwise entail—some of the stumbling-blocks of the past.

But it is true? How can we even find out if it is true, without special pleading or telling the scientist how to do his job?

If it *is* true, then sometimes at least Christians would be in a position to predict the results of scientific discovery. Let us pose this question deliberately. Can Christianity predict the results of a scientific investigation?

If the agnostics, atheists and humanists are right, or even the Christians who deny that science and Christianity can have intimate contact—then the answer to this question must be an emphatic *No*. But if the traditional Christian position is right, then such prediction *ought* to be possible sometimes, in principle at least. If this could be shown to be so, then we should not only have a valuable confirmatory line of evidence in favour of the truth of Christianity, but we should forge an important link between religious and secular thought.

PREDICTION IN SCIENCE

How shall we apply the test? Let us first be clear about terms.

What do we mean by prediction? We may look to science for help here. In science prediction means *anticipation*. Unless our theory has reached a stage of high sophistication (as in astronomy, after centuries of experience) we do not claim near certainty. Indeed, we learn from the history of science that successful predictions have sometimes been used in support of false theories, and that true theories have sometimes been discarded because they seemingly led to predictions which proved false.

In like manner a Christian who, on the basis of his faith, predicts the outcome of a scientific investigation (or conversely, a scientist who on the basis of his science predicts the outcome of a theological investigation) must not be dogmatic. His theory—the theory that the Author of Nature and of the Christian revelation are one and the same—may lead him to expect that scientific discovery in a particular field will follow a certain course, but dogmatism in a given case is uncalled for. Nevertheless, as in science, it is fair to claim that on the whole the correctness of a theory is suggested by its power to predict.

Our appreciation today of the fallibility of prediction throws a flood of light on the history of the warfare of science and religion.

The Middle Ages left mankind with a legacy of dogmatism. Indeed, when we read the old books today we can hardly restrain the thought, which recurs again and again: *How can you be so sure?* This dogmatic attitude pervaded theology, as it did every other discipline, but at the beginning of the modern era it encountered its first setback in science. Theological dogmatism, however, was as yet untouched and, naturally enough, theologians tended to express themselves over-dogmatically in discussing the newly developing sciences. They tended to express themselves extremely dogmatically about astronomy, geology, evolution, genetics and so on—often reasserting traditional views which had been held for thousands of years with little change. Sometimes they virtually told scientists what they *ought* to discover. But before science had progressed very far, it began to appear that some of these views were wrong. For example, the earth is not the centre of the universe after all, and children inherit their bodies both from the male and female parents, not from the male only as had been supposed. It seemed, therefore, that on a number of issues theological expectations about the facts of science had turned out wrong. So the view that Christianity can predict the course of discovery came into disrepute. From this it was a short step to the conclusion that, in future, it would be safer and wiser to keep science and religion well apart.

Our earlier argument, then, was made invalid because we overlooked the difference between certainty and expectation. We imagined a man who pinned his faith on one particular theory of science with no room for doubt that his religion really demanded *that* theory and no other: no room for doubt that the facts of science likewise warranted the view that *that* theory alone was true. Of course he would have suffered spiritually if the theory had turned out to be false. But if we think of not one theory but many, and not of certainty but of probability, the man would not have been in so sore a plight.

Similarly, a chemist does not lose faith in Dalton's atomic

theory because an analysis shows that the compound of chlorine and water does not contain its two ingredients in simple molecular proportions.[1] The universe in which we live is incredibly complicated and our simple laws and expectations are bound to have endless exceptions. But it remains true on the whole that, if the laws we formulate are right, they will successfully predict the general course of discovery.

When once we abandon the old dogmatism, we see that if Christianity is objectively true, then there ought to be a connexion between religion and science—indeed, between religion and everything else in man's experience. But we must not be unduly distressed if things turn out unexpectedly now and then—or indeed quite often—provided it is clear that our predictions are successful with a greater than chance expectation.

Can we put this idea to the test? So far as the future is concerned we must wait and see, but as regards the past it is otherwise. Let us look at some of the controversies in which science has been involved and ask how they were resolved in fact, and how we might have expected them to have been resolved according to non-Christian and Christian insight respectively.

[1] A molecule of chlorine combines with between 7·10 and 7·44 molecules of water, the composition varying. *Jour. Chem. Soc.*, 1959, p. 4131.

CHAPTER 3

HOW MUCH CAN SCIENCE EXPLAIN?

LET US START OUR INVESTIGATION AT THE SIMPLEST level possible. One of the most insistent predictions of the rationalist has been, and often still is, that as knowledge advances, so it will become increasingly apparent that science is invading every field of human inquiry; that no phenomena lie outside its range. Because we can thus confidently expect that science will explain all features of the world we live in, he says, there is no need to believe in God or other supernatural agencies.

IMAGINED CONVERSATION

To bring our thoughts to a focus let us imagine how an atheist and a Christian might have conversed in the latter part of the nineteenth century. The atheist has put his case as we have stated it above. In reply the Christian says that he also expects science to develop, but he is sure that as it does so its limitations will become increasingly apparent. Science will throw light on many unexplained phenomena but it will rarely, if ever, explain away features of our world which Christians have traditionally believed to be due to the intervention of God. Rather it will help to bring the reasons for belief in God into the clear light of day.

To our atheist, of course, these remarks seem highly obscurantist. Science, he says, provides clear intelligible explanations, but when we introduce God we abandon hope of understanding anything. No one knows, or can know, how or why God did this or that. To bring Him into the argument solves no problems, for if we claim, say, that God made the world then (as John Stuart Mill's father taught him when he was still a boy—quoted with approval by Bertrand Russell[1]) you would have to ask the question, "Who made God?", which cannot be answered.

[1] *Why I am not a Christian*, 1927 (Reprinted 1957).

Science, our atheist continues, shows us how man's thinking can be rescued from metaphysics—from the untestable hypothesis. You can observe the heavens to find out if the earth goes round the sun, but no conceivable experiment or observation will tell you if God created the heavens and the earth. Unless metaphysics is abolished, there can be no steady progress in human thinking, for there can be no checks on whether new opinions are right or wrong. The probability that new error has crept in will, in fact, be increased whenever an attempt is made to develop a metaphysical argument.

And so the argument continues—with the Christian, perhaps, on the defensive.

Science has advanced beyond all expectation and much has been written on the meaning and philosophy of science over the past half-century, with the result that many issues have become clarified. We are now in a position to say something about how the scales have turned. Have the developments in science confirmed what the atheist thought would happen, or was the Christian right after all?

EXPLANATION

Let us first consider the claims of science to *explain* events, for here lies the crux of the matter.

We may start by imagining a simple experiment. Let us take a piece of wire—a tungsten wire of the kind used for the filament of an ordinary electric lamp will serve very well. (A filament consists of a single crystal and is, so far as we can discover, *completely* uniform.) We hold its ends and *pull* until it breaks. But we cannot —and this is the important point—we *cannot* tell beforehand *where* it will break. With a truly uniform wire this will depend (we suppose) on chance movements of atoms and electrons: it is quite unpredictable.

But not everything about the breaking of the wire is unpredictable. If we know the weight of the wire before it breaks, we can predict that it will have the same weight afterwards. We may well be able to predict by how much the wire will have stretched at its breaking point, likewise its electrical resistance, its density, its colour and so on. But still there is one thing at least which we cannot predict—at what position along its length it will break.

Our simple experiment illustrates a point which has become fundamental in science over the past half century. In ordinary language it is the principle that the last straw breaks the camel's back. Observation and experiment—science in fact—can tell us a lot about camels with broken backs, but if we steadily pile one straw on another upon the beast of burden, it cannot tell us exactly when or where the back will break.

We must not, of course, take this rule so literally as to apply it to real camels—we need rather to think of imaginary camels about the size of atoms! Science can tell us a lot about a disintegrated radium atom, but not when a particular atom will disintegrate; about the shining of a distant star, but not when a photon from that star will enter my eye; about snowflakes, but not about what a particular snowflake will be like. It would be easy to multiply examples.

What we find is that there are *some* features of phenomena about which science enables us, on the basis of past experience, to make successful predictions, but often there are others which seem to be caused by the equivalent of the last straw. With these we can only be wise *after* the event. We can make a plausible guess as to what *may* have happened—but we cannot say for certain what *did* happen. Science in its strict sense cannot help us; it is difficult or impossible to do experiments or make observations with a view to finding out if our guesses are right or wrong. We may call our guesses *explanations* if we please: it is matter of words. But if we do so, we must remember that they are explanations of a weak and unconvincing kind.

METAPHYSICS IN SCIENCE

Now the atheist has always insisted that, as science comes in at the front door so to speak, metaphysics must go out at the back. And by metaphysics he means that which cannot be tested—assertions like the one that God made the world or that He intervened in this or that event. But today we are finding that science itself cannot get along without metaphysics. Increasingly we find that modern guesses about the universe, about the ultimate nature of matter and about the origins of things are tending to be metaphysical in the sense that we cannot do experiments or make observations to find out if they are true.

#2 The progress of science itself gives us a more open picture of the world than we had before. Though science offers us no *direct* proof that God is at the back of nature, it has destroyed the old determinism which seemed to rule out this possibility.

This is hardly what the atheist expected would happen, but the Christian is not surprised.

INVADING EVERY FIELD

Let us now look at the claim that science can invade every field of human inquiry. By now it will be clear that claims of this kind invite misunderstanding. When the word "scientific" is used the ordinary man associates it with the sciences of physics, astronomy chemistry and engineering—the branches of science which make it possible to predict what is going to happen, that tell you when and where the next eclipse will be visible, how many kilowatts of electricity can be made in a power-station when so much coal is burnt, or how much steel you need to build a bridge to carry a certain load.

But if we include after-the-event explanations, when we say that science will invade the whole of knowledge, it is apparent that we are using a single form of words to cover two very different meanings. It is one thing to say that you can predict an eclipse; it is quite another to say that after an eclipse has taken place unexpectedly you can invent a reason to explain why it happened. Nevertheless, even though it may be far removed from exact science, a suggested explanation of an unexpected eclipse would be well worth making.

The case is very different when we make the wide claim that after-the-event explanations can account for *everything*. Objectively the assertion is now quite meaningless (apart from being tautologous)—it may tell us something about ourselves, but it tells us nothing about the outside world. For it is an accepted principle that for a statement to have meaning it must be possible to contrast it with the opposite statement. "Crocodiles shed tears" has meaning because we can imagine crocodiles which do not shed tears. But "Everything is everything" has no meaning because it does not stand in contrast to "Everything is not everything". which is unthinkable.

In what sense, then, can we understand the statement, "Science can in principle account for everything"? If we mean science in its *strict* sense, the statement is meaningful but false. But if we include in our science after-the-event speculations, then the statement does not affirm anything at all. For if I say that science cannot account for this or that, mentioning something definite for which I think it has no answer, the materialist will at once start speculating to prove me wrong. And this he can *always* do. It is *always* possible to find some scientific principle of our choice which *might* explain *anything*. By merely asserting that X cannot be explained scientifically, I make my assertion untrue—that is if I think of science in its wider sense.

If anyone doubts this, he may immediately convince himself of its truth by suggesting something that *might* be beyond the scope of science. We soon find that we can immediately suggest explanations (with the help of suitable scientific jargon) as to why, say, stars should form; why there should be planets capable of supporting life; why dead matter should become alive in the early ages of the earth's history; why evolution should produce all the species including man; why "emergent" properties of mind, such as consciousness, love, hate, or even ghosts (explained as "hallucinations") should turn up when the brain becomes sufficiently complicated; why natural selection should bring about everything that is helpful for survival, and so on endlessly.

EXPLAINING EVERYTHING

Not only can we produce these pseudo-scientific "explanations" for everything that has happened in the past or will happen in the future, but we can explain everything that has *not* happened also— just in case it does! If a kettle should freeze when we put it on the fire, or monkeys should produce the plays of Shakespeare by thumping on the keys of typewriters, we shall at once be able to explain these events by saying that on statistical grounds they were bound to happen occasionally, if rarely, and that no doubt we have witnessed a rare fluctuation!

L. P. Jacks illustrated the point in the following way.[1] He is alone in his room and about to retire for the night. Suddenly he notices a strong odour of Manilla cigars. It lasts for a few minutes and then goes. Later he talks to a young scientist about this. "Oh," says the man, "you must have left your window open and there was a policeman on his beat outside who had waited a few minutes for a smoke." "But the window was shut", explains Jacks. "No, it could not have been, you must have made a mistake, you only thought it was shut." "But the house was in a lonely spot far off from any policeman's beat." "Yes, but that night was an exception: the policeman would naturally have chosen a lonely spot for his unlawful smoke" . . . and so on. There is no end to it, for if we are at liberty to invent untestable explanations as and when we please, it is obvious that we can explain everything.

Now if we are in a position to explain everything that has happened, or even that has not happened, by means of after-the-event guesses (whether these be couched in scientific jargon or not), then it is mere tautology to say that there is no limit to science. The statement tells us nothing at all. Or if it does it tells us about ourselves: for the opposite statement can only mean that people are too dull-witted to invent explanations, and that tells us something about people, not about science or about nature.

EVOLUTION

It is worth illustrating this point with reference to evolution—for here—if anywhere, science is supposed to have had enormous success. Indeed, it is often claimed that the theory of evolution knocked the design argument on the head, so removing one of the chief arguments for belief in God.

Evolutionary explanations are almost entirely of the after-the-event kind. The camel has a hump and this like everything else is due to natural selection which we are told offers "a scientific rational mechanistic explanation". Maybe, but if the camel had no hump, the explanation would be the same. The cat has a tail and natural selection tells us why. But if puss had no tail, natural selection would explain that too. If an animal has a feature which

[1] L. P. Jacks, *The Confessions of an Octogenarian*, 1942, p. 237.

seems to confer no obvious advantage, we are told that it must have an advantage or it would not be there. If difficulties are raised we are told that the advantage lies in some other factor with which the first is linked genetically and *oleiogenes* are invented for the purpose. (These are genes which affect more than one factor in the progeny, with perhaps only one of the factors selected.) If a feature which would be useful to an animal is *not* there, then of course natural selection explains this too. And so on, whatever the facts to be explained.

Natural selection is a valid theory. It has been observed to operate in nature (e.g. in the dark colour which some moths take on in an industrial area) and also in the laboratory. So when we apply the principle to nature the picture we paint is plausible. Nevertheless it does not get us very far. After all, natural selection also determines which cars remain on the roads after a lapse of years and which disappear, but this does not tell us how the models are manufactured. No one has shown that chance changes in molecules followed by natural selection created the wonderful structures which we see in nature, and the idea is not very plausible. If, nevertheless, we insist that it is true, there is still nothing we can do to prove our case. It is an after-the-event guess. Apart from the fact that scientific jargon is used and that our prejudices favour this kind of guess, it has no better status than the equally untestable statement that God created things as they are.

AN END OF THINKING?

To this, it is no answer to say that God is an end of thinking because we cannot ask, *Who made God?* For the same difficulties apply in evolution, as indeed in all science. We may say, no doubt correctly, that the difference between one generation and the next is caused by random selection and mutation of genes—sometimes we can even see the change in a chromosome under the microscope. But why does a gene change? Perhaps a cosmic ray hits it—an after-the-event guess once more. But where does the cosmic ray particle come from and why does it hit the chromosome so as to alter it in a particular way? . . . We can continue thus, making further guesses—but as we build guess upon guess the chances that we are right become more and more slender, the very objection which the atheist raises against theism. All scientific explanations must go back and back endlessly, with more and more assumptions entering at each stage.

The position we are coming to seems to be this, that pushed back far enough ideas of cause and effect are mental: it is *we* who cause our muscles to move, our mouths to speak. When we have nailed down the cause of an event to the action of a person, we do not usually wish to ask further questions (unless they be psychological ones, relating to the person himself). No doubt all our thinking is limited—after all why should we expect to be able to understand everything in the universe? But ultimately explanations in terms of mind—including God's mind—are more satisfying than any others we are likely to find. But here, perhaps, we are on debatable ground.

This much, however, is certain. If we make very wide claims for science, they cease to be claims at all. At best we are only claiming, as did the schoolmen in the Middle Ages, that our minds are so very nimble that they are never at a loss for an answer!

CONCLUSION

How far, then, has science fulfilled the expectations of the nine-teenth-century sceptic, or his Christian friend? The sceptic has proved right in saying that scientists have become much cleverer in the art of inventing after-the-event guesses. Indeed, since the development of the social sciences, science can claim 100 per cent success in this field. But as the guesses are often implausible (at least to those who think critically) and are often highly metaphysical, it is untrue that they destroy the metaphysics of theology. You cannot destroy one form of metaphysics by another on the ground that the first is less "scientific". As for the claim that science would one day enable everything to be explained scientifically without resource to spiritual powers, the sceptic's victory, if victory it be, is a hollow one. It belongs to the realm of semantics —to the use of words—not to the discovery of new facts.

But what about belief in God? Here there is no agreement as yet. The Christian who predicted that scientific evidence for belief in God might one day become compelling would certainly be disappointed today. At the same time he would be reassured by the fact that the *reasons* for belief in God have not been undermined and he would note that the astonishing increase in the number and variety of after-the-event guesses in recent years are suggestive of a thinly disguised theophobia. In Russia, he would note, there is no disguise at all: the avowed objective of the new speculations in Communist countries is to prove that there is no God.

The sceptic expected science to destroy metaphysics. Here his prediction is badly out: he little suspected that in the end science itself would become as metaphysical as theology. But so it has happened, and the trend continues. Such an outcome is very much along the lines which the Christian might have expected.

Putting all the recent developments together, if he could return to view the scene, the Christian would be much saddened, but at no point would he feel that his predictions were badly wrong. The sceptic, on the other hand, though (if militant) he might be pleased to observe the decline in theology, would not be reassured by the turn things have taken in scientific thought.

CHAPTER 4

DO GAPS CLOSE?

GAPS—TWO KINDS

IT HAS LONG BEEN HELD BY ATHEISTS AND AGNOSTICS that as knowledge advances so events, which were formerly attributed to the action of God, are one by one incorporated into science. As the gaps in our knowledge close up, so God is pushed farther and farther into the background: when all have closed He will cease to be a necessary part of man's thinking. Christians, on the other hand, have never expected God to be pushed out of His universe in this or any other way!

The Christian view is sometimes misunderstood and needs a word of explanation. It is sometimes supposed that Christians think of a miracle as an event which cannot be explained by science, but this is not quite accurate. Christians recognize two kinds of events for which science cannot find reasonably plausible explanations—we use the word "explanations" in a popular and inexact sense. The first is due to our ignorance, and many gaps of this kind may be expected to close slowly with the progress of knowledge. But the Christian also thinks that *some* unexplained events are due to real intervention by God or spiritual beings, and he expects these to remain outside the sphere of science. In fact, the more these are studied, the more difficult it should be to find acceptable scientific explanations for them.

If, therefore, the Christian is right, we should expect some gaps in knowledge to show signs of closing, while others should widen. But if the secularists are right, we may expect all gaps to close in the end: there would seem to be no reason why some should widen, though many might remain unchanged for a long time.

Considering the question from the Christian angle, how might gaps of the two kinds be distinguished? Apart from revelation, it must often be a case of "Wait and see". But not everyone is content to leave the solution of problems till long after he is dead. From time to time Christians inevitably try their hand at deciding *which* events are of the second kind. Being fallible they can, and do, make mistakes. So the Christian will not be surprised if it sometimes happens that a gap which he expected to become wider in fact becomes narrower—and the converse might also happen. But by and large the difference between the Christian and the secular expectation would remain.

Let us look at some of the unsolved problems which have puzzled people in the past and see how they have fared.

GRAVITY

Some familiar examples are found in the early days of science. Sir Isaac Newton explained the movements of the planets around the sun by his theory of gravity but eventually came to the conclusion that the solar system could not continue for ever if gravity alone was operating. Every now and again, he thought, when the accumulation of small perturbations brought the cosmic clock too far from its norm, God would have to step in to restore the *status quo*. But Laplace was later able to show that this 'gap' in the scientific picture could be bridged by science. Newton's Law was in reality more powerful and had wider ramifications than had been suspected. It was not necessary, after all, to suppose that God intervened. "I have no need of that hypothesis," he said to Napoleon—a remark which was not intended to mean that he disbelieved in God, but that God was not a useful hypothesis for solving problems in astronomy.

But the gap which puzzled the Newtonians most of all was the hiatus between gravity and matter. How could matter act on other matter with which it was not in contact or indeed connected by any detectable physical means? Here again it was suggested by some that it was God who made this happen. This was the view held, for example, by William Whiston who succeeded Newton in his Professorial chair at Cambridge.[1] Here was a gap—a very literal gap this time!—the gap between two objects across which,

[1] W. Whiston, *A New Theory of the Earth*. "The universal force of gravitation being so plainly above, besides, and contrary to the Nature of Matter . . . must be the Effect of a Divine Power and Efficacy which governs the whole world . . .", 1708 ed., p. 6.

contrary to all reason, an influence passes which "tells" one of the existence of the other. What has happened to this "gap" since Newton's day?

The answer seems to be: Nothing at all. We still do not understand the nature of space, or know how gravity operates. Nevertheless, few people today would claim that this gap ought to be filled by God—except perhaps in the sense that God upholds the universe and so *all* physical phenomena. God does not seem to foot the bill at all; gravity is altogether too impersonal a force to be attributed directly to a personal God, and it is only one of several seemingly independent forces which are transmitted through space. Later we shall discuss gravity again in another connexion (Chapter 9).

So much for two classical examples. Though they puzzled learned men in their time, they can hardly have bothered ordinary Christians of the day. Newton's conjecture about the solar system was a private speculation of his own and the notion that gravity is the finger of God, though it appealed to some, seems always to have had its critics.

Thus, in one case the gap has narrowed or even disappeared; in the other it remains largely unchanged, though the possibility (if ever there *was* a serious possibility) of putting God in the gap has perhaps diminished.

BEGINNING OF THE UNIVERSE

It would be unwise to generalize from these instances. We ought rather to consider examples which in the past were widely taken by Christians as evidence of belief in God. If we confine ourselves to science, these are chiefly concerned with the creative epochs of nature.

The origin of the universe illustrates the traditional "gap" better, perhaps, than any other topic. Whatever science may say about the present world, so the argument ran, it cannot tell us how the world started, and our lack of knowledge constitutes a "gap"[1] which must be filled by God.

[1] The choice of the word "gap" in connexion with topics as yet untouched by science is not a happy one. Strictly speaking there should be something *on each side* of a gap and this is not so with beginnings. However, even in other

How did the universe start? The common answer of atheists, since early times, has been that it did *not* start. From eternity backwards there was always a vast concourse of atoms, a primordial matter, out of which things formed themselves by chance. (Ancient believers in a god or gods accepted the primordial material, but maintained that a god intervened in order to create order out of chaos.[1] Ancient Stoics argued against ancient atheists that the wonderful design we see in nature could not have come about fortuitously.[2]

In modern times atheists have not done much better. J. B. S. Haldane, in his *Possible Worlds* (1928), argued that by sheer chance chaotic matter must organize itself again and again because there is infinite time available. In fact everything has happened and will happen again and again in eternity. The atheist can always close this "gap" in our knowledge about the beginning of things by indulging in speculations of this kind.

What, then, has happened to the "gap" today? There is no doubt that as knowledge increases it has become not easier but vastly harder to close it up by plausible scientific theory.

In the first place philosophical thinking about the principles of science—a result chiefly of the quantum theory—has revealed a limitation in the scope of scientific explanation. As we have already noted (Chapter 3) it is meaningless to talk of scientific explanation at all today, if what one really has in mind is a scheme of so-called explanations which would explain *anything* and *everything* whether it has happened or not!

---

[1] e.g. Cicero. *Of the Nature of the Gods*, Book II, where the argument is used that letters thrown down at random on the floor do not produce literature.

[2] See A. O. Lovejoy, G. Boas *et al, Primitivism and Related Ideas in Antiquity*, Baltimore, 1935.

---

connexions the use of the word is objectionable because it begs the question. Suppose, for example, a new animal occurs for the first time in the geological record, produced *either* by natural means from some unknown previously existing animal, or by supernatural means, i.e. as a special creation. Then to speak of a "gap" implies natural means—for the animal must then be connected with animals which went before as well as with those which followed after.

CHANCE VERSUS SCIENCE

Secondly, we now realize much more clearly than in the past that "sheer chance" arguments are destructive of the very science on which they purport to depend. It turns out that all our scientific laws are based on the assumption that just anything does *not* happen and that when once we begin to invoke the long arm of coincidence we destroy science itself at its roots. If water boils at 100° C., or the polar ice-caps melt, or the year remains at constant length, or salt and silver nitrate react, it is no answer to say that just occasionally events like these *must* happen anyway by sheer chance. Such talk undermines all scientific understanding, for it sets up a barrier to the discovery of nature's laws. To illustrate the point, let us consider the observation that water boils at 100° C. How could we bring this fact within the ambit of science if anti-scientists won the day with such arguments as the following:

> Water might boil at *any* temperature if it boils at all when it is heated. If the universe has existed for an infinitude of years, then by chance water must have boiled at all conceivable temperatures in the past and it will boil at all conceivable temperatures in the future. Over the past century or so it has often been observed to boil at 100° C. (at atmospheric pressure) but this period only covers an *infinitely* small fraction of total time. We must not therefore take it as representative of what might happen over long cosmic periods, far less of the universal laws of the universe. If we were to choose random epochs in cosmic history we should find that it boiled sometimes at one temperature and sometimes at another in a random way. It is true that there is a high probability that it will not boil at the same temperature for any length of time. Yet because time is infinite it will in fact boil at any given temperature for an infinitesimally short period, say a few centuries or millenniums, not just once but an infinite number of times. It is wrong therefore to look for some law, or set of scientific explanations, to explain why it boils at 100° C. at the present time.

Obviously this line of reasoning, which may be carried through for *any* natural event, or any observation whatever, would (if taken seriously) make science impossible. If nature behaves in a random way, then we cannot learn her laws for there are no laws to learn. In fact all science depends on the assumption that the arm of coincidence is *not* long, but quite short; that no explanation which falls back on highly improbable coincidence in a case of difficulty can claim to be scientific.

If, then, we try to explain our universe in terms of a random fluctuation of some kind, we might as well *not* explain it at all. It is disingenuous to use scientific jargon and at the same time abandon the scientific way of thinking.[1]

THE BEGINNING—THEORIES

But what about the concrete suggestions which have been put forward about what might have happened when the universe began?

It has often been suggested that a chaotic gas formed itself into worlds, and so the cosmos came into being. We now see that though there is no particular objection (in principle) to the view that the stars condensed from a gas, it is highly fraudulent if put forward as an explanation of the universe. For the chaotic gas could not have been truly chaotic: rather it must, in the sense of thermodynamics, have been *more* ordered than the system into which it turned. Entropy, the mathematical measure of disorder, increases in all physical processes and the condensation into worlds would have been one of these processes.

Similarly, there is the suggestion that the universe expands and contracts rhythmically, but that now it is in the phase of expansion. If this is true, then the same principle must hold—creative or antichance events will not take place. If we think scientifically, then we must hold that the universe as it oscillates between its two states—condensed and expanded—will become less and less ordered in the process. Oscillation cannot, therefore, be eternal.

Fortunately a certain amount of scientific evidence is now available on this topic—though the picture may, of course, change in future years. Most astronomers now agree that the evidence for the expansion of the universe is overwhelming. Since the

---

[1] For other arguments, notably that of P. W. Bridgman, against the random fluctuation theory, see R. E. D. Clark, *The Universe Plan or Accident*, 1961, pp. 32 ff.

steady-state theories of the universe have now lost much of their plausibility, we may extrapolate backwards in time. This brings us to an epoch when all matter in the universe was highly condensed, at a colossal temperature and density. If the primeval fireball consisted of electrons and protons (hydrogen) at the start, calculations indicate that there would have been considerable conversion to helium. The actual proportion of helium in the universe (20–25 per cent) appears to be around the expected amount, which suggests that the universe can only have exploded once. In addition it has been possible to detect a background radiation of radio waves and this also is in agreement with the theory that the whole universe was once concentrated in a single fire-ball. Again, if such an explosion had taken place many times, the background of radiation would, it seems, be much larger than it is. The evidence, therefore, as so far as it goes, points to an expansion of a fireball which started some thousands of millions of years ago: there is no indication that our universe is in a state of oscillation. All avenues of thought which might enable us, by science only, to explore what might have happened before the fire-ball began to explode seem to be barred.

We have been thinking of the origin of the universe in terms of a theory widely accepted at the time of writing. But obviously the same considerations must apply to other theories. If, for example, atoms are created individually and continuously—we shall eventually be flawed if we ask how they are created, or how that which creates them is created. Science will never fill the "gap" at the beginning of things.

EXTRAPOLATING TO INFINITY

In the past atheists have often argued that considerations of this kind ought to be discounted on the ground that the universe as a whole is too big a subject for man's intellect to master. We must not extrapolate from the finite to the infinite.

We are free to argue thus if we please. But if we do so we must remember that what the argument amounts to is simply this— that the scientific gap in our knowledge about the beginning of the universe has not been and never will be closed by science. In fact, we have now made the gap *infinitely* great because unless we extrapolate science cannot be applied at all! So the risk that God will be squeezed out is no longer formidable!

It has become fashionable in recent years to stress the dangers of extrapolating from our limited experience to the universe at large. And of course there *are* dangers. But it is well to remind ourselves that were it not for extrapolation of this kind, science could have made little headway in the past. The ancients thought there were two kinds of matter, *terrestrial and celestial,* and this mistake arose at least partly because they were fearful of extrapolating from matter on earth to matter in the sky!

ORDER IN CHEMISTRY

In all discussions of this kind we seem forced to think of the universe as starting off as a highly ordered system—measured in terms of negative entropy (negentropy) the order of the primitive fire-ball must have been quite fantastic. But order takes many other forms than that of "availability for doing mechanical work". Do we find evidence of other forms of order in the universe?

There is no doubt that we do. When we study biology we soon come to realize that life is only possible in a universe suited to its existence.

This means among other things that many of the atoms must be so designed that they will be capable of fulfilling the role which they will subsequently play in living organisms. And their simple compounds, too, such as carbon dioxide, water, and phosphoric acid must have properties which are compatible, biologically speaking, with one another. In this field many wonderful correlations, many wonderful examples of "order", have come to light.[1] We note that, in this connexion, there can be no question whatever of explaining the order by evolution or survival of the fittest. For the atoms were there before there was such a thing as natural selection, nor do their properties change with time.

Nearly two centuries ago chemists were beginning to realize how wonderfully adapted were the properties of water for the

[1] L. J. Henderson, *The Fitness of the Environment,* 1913; *The Order of Nature,* 1917; A. E. Needham, *The Uniqueness of Biological Materials,* 1965; R. E. D. Clark, *The Universe Plan or Accident,* 3rd ed., 1961; J. C. Speakman, *Molecules,* 1966.

needs of life—they were impressed by its property of becoming less dense when it freezes, with its maximum density at 4° C., and so on. Such facts were used in older books (e.g. the *Bridgewater Treatises*) as an argument that atoms had been designed by God. There is a trivial sense, of course, in which it may be said that these or some of these properties may now be explained by science—we can, for example, explain how the crystal structure of ice arises, but this only pushes the problem back a stage or two. These amazing properties, so rare in chemistry, are necessary for the wellbeing of life and often for its very existence, but are quite beyond the ken of any acceptable scientific explanation.

A good example of recent thinking in this field is afforded by the phosphate group, the unique properties of which (high energy phosphate bonds, etc.) make it irreplaceable in the living organism. In addition phosphate precipitates with calcium to give a complex calcium phosphate, *hydroxyapatite*, of exceptional strength, crystals of which are formed in the collagen fibres of bone owing to a surprising coincidence in the unit crystal size and repeat lengths of the two materials. This bone ensures a reservoir of phosphate in the body and helps to maintain a steady phosphate concentration in body fluids.

The hydroxyapatite has curious electrical properties: it generates a voltage when a bone is bent. The potential acts in such a way that the phosphate dissolves where it is not needed and redeposits where the bone needs strengthening. Hydroxyapatite also picks up flouride ions forming flourapatite, an exceedingly hard material, which forms the enamel of teeth.

This elaborate dovetailing of properties *might* be coincidental, but if so it is difficult to resist the thought that coincidence might account for anything!

Somehow, then, the many extraordinary properties of the chemical elements must have been built into the primeval fireball! How did these astonishing instances of order arise? A gap in scientific knowledge? We may call it that if we please, but if we are discerning we shall not talk glibly about the risk that God will get squeezed out when the gap is closed! The gap becomes larger as science advances, as we learn more about the order in the chemical elements. Science on the other hand has not yet given us a single hint, however implausible, as to how the gap could be closed up, even fractionally. The fact is that genuine gaps in knowledge of the kind which Christians—and even pagans before them—have always recognized as evidence of plan in the universe show no sign of closing up in the twentieth century—which is of course what any Christian might have predicted.

In a later chapter (Chapter 16) we shall discuss, briefly, some of the other so-called gaps. We shall see that they also lead to similar conclusions.

CHAPTER 5

FEED-BACK IN SCIENCE

WHAT WE DO OFTEN REACTS BACK UPON US, CAUSING us to change our future behaviour. It is the same with the activity we call science—the results of science and the thinking of scientists affect the future of science.

OPTIMISM OF THE 30's

For the secularists the prospects for science were rosy from the start. There seemed no doubt, at least until the 30's, that science—and more particularly the scientific way of thinking—could solve man's problems. The Russian Revolution floated on a wave of scientific enthusiasm, which rapidly created an industrial nation out of a primitive peasant society. The Japanese, primitive till 1900, felt able to conquer the world by 1940. In the West, optimism was boundless—the writings of H. G. Wells sold in millions and were absorbed with semi-religious enthusiasm by a rising generation who came to believe that Christianity was no longer important, in fact quite harmful. All man had to do was to rid the world of superstition, and teach the masses to apply the methods of science to everyday affairs. If this could be done, crime would diminish, wars would cease—sensible men would not wish to fight one another—and mankind could look forward to a million years of peace and increasing happiness.

What of over-population? This would be no problem at all, for science had already made two ears of wheat grow where one grew before—and without doubt it could repeat the trick on a wide front, almost without limit. Increasing use of machinery would ensure that no one need work very hard to keep the wheels of production turning. Indeed, the chief problem was not work but leisure; study groups were started in earnest so that people might know how to fill the vacant hours.

It was feared in some quarters that the prospects for man might not be so rosy after all. What if the sun, suddenly and without warning, should become a *nova*, so reducing the earth to a cinder? Obligingly, the astronomers came out with comforting news. They discovered that the sun was less than half-way on its evolutionary course and, all being well, should shine quietly in the sky for a few thousand million years.

One further point, however, continued to bother many people. In time, scientists said, the universe was doomed to an entropic heat-death. Though far off, this possibility grated against the exuberant optimism of the day. It seemed too much like an unpleasant maggot at the bottom of the jam-pot, so people listened eagerly to those public men who, being quite ignorant of thermodynamic theory, felt competent to assure their hearers that the law of entropy had no cosmic relevance.

So much for the grandiose humanistic thought of the 30's. Christian beliefs were different. The optimism of a Christian is tempered by a sense of realism, for he believes that every project done in man's own power without the help of God will end in frustration—the biblical "vanity". Science is good in itself, but man has not the wisdom to manage the vast forces it unleashes. Until he learns, in sincere humility, to ask for God's aid, his projects will fail.

NEW VIEWS ON SCIENCE

For Christians, one of the saddest features of the modern rise of science was the fact that, only too often, those who became leaders in the scientific field, were using the laboratory as a refuge from religion. Many of the agnostic and atheist scientists of the 30's had been brought up as Christians but had reacted strongly. There seemed little doubt that scientific views, not only in Russia (where the point is not questioned) but even in the West, were beginning to be coloured by atheism—just as, centuries before, they had been coloured by religion. This applied particularly to the philosophy of science. A new philosophy of science began to develop which, in the end, would react back upon science, making it less beautiful, less inspiring, less worth while. The Christian could see that the secularist, despite the very ardour with which he put forward scientific solutions for every problem, would in the end hurt the science he cherished because his basic philosophy was wrong: and in the end he would be disillusioned by the science in which he trusted.

For what determines how we think of science? This must depend on how far science links up with our basic religious needs; on how far it can satisfy deep emotions, or lead to greater truths outside itself. The same is true of all human endeavour. An artist who came to think of his work as mere blotches of coloured chemicals on canvas and nothing more would be disillusioned in art: a musician who thought only of vibrating wires or compressions and rarefactions passing through air would cease to find inspiration in music.

Now this is the effect which the new theories of our century, coloured by atheism, must inevitably have. Between the wars the theory that science does not expect to discover truth about nature —indeed, that there is no such thing as *absolute* truth, took firm root. Science ceased to be a matter of thinking God's thoughts after Him: its aim, the new generation said, was to make our sensations consistent with one another—in fact to indulge an academic hobby. The older idea that science, in showing us the wonders of nature, would reveal to us something of the power and glory of God, could not be brought into line with the new aim of science and was abandoned. Logical positivists and their fellow-travellers argued that concepts, such as God, life, soul, etc., which did not admit of experimental verification or measurement, were meaningless, and it was argued that knowledge was concerned much more with quantity than with quality. The Christian saw mankind as the trustee of nature which he was commanded to subdue and control: with the new secular outlook in vogue, the stewardship was forgotten.

In view of these facts, no Christian could feel over-optimistic with regard to the prospects which faced mankind. Even the more thoughtful secularists began to sense some of the dangers: they began to talk of man's physical evolution outstripping his moral evolution.

THE SPECTRE OF SCIENCE TODAY

As we look back today, we can see in one field after another, that the Christian was right and the secularist wrong. Though grateful for the benefits it bestows, mankind is now frightened, almost terrified, of science. But there is no going back.

One horrifying discovery has been the lack of loyalty and morality amongst scientists and technicians themselves. Almost as a matter of course the rocket experts who loyally worked for Hitler at Peenemunde changed sides and worked for Americans or Russians. Nazi doctors experimented on human victims; atomic bombs were developed as weapons and used on civilians.

Men fear increasingly that armies of scientists and technicians, almost trigger-happy, are irreparably upsetting the balance of nature. An atomic bomb exploded in space has altered the van Allen belts which encircle our earth and they will not return to normal for a generation. Needles have been put into orbit and create difficulties for radio-astronomers. The burnt fuel of rockets may before long greatly alter the composition of the very high atmosphere with unforseeable consequences. Insecticides are blamed for producing the "silent spring" and contamination by DDT is now worldwide—it can be detected, even, in fish caught near the Antarctic Continent. New drugs not only compel the State to provide for hundreds of tragically deformed children, but create problems of addiction of such magnitude that they seem quite insoluble. New scientific instruments, ruthlessly applied in the fishing industry, are depleting the seas of fish and threatening, even, to exterminate whales altogether. Science applied on the land, makes new deserts and enlarges old ones.[1] And always, when remedies are applied, the story is the same: too little is done too late.

The results of these developments are inevitable: we are witnessing them today in the increasing unpopularity of science. Divorced from religion, science cannot supply the motives which make life, or science itself, worth while, nor can it guarantee that knowledge will not be used destructively. Curiosity and discovery which do not point to something beyond themselves will not

[1] G. V. Jacks and R. O. Whyte, (*The Rape of the Earth*, 1939—still a standard text) estimated that man had added a million square miles of desert to the world with huge further areas approaching desert conditions. According to more recent reports (See *New Scientist* 6 June, 1957, p. 29) arid zones are still spreading. Christians will recall the land laws of the Old Testament— effectively designed to stop erosion.

touch the springs of life. No man in his senses will, for the love of the thing, devote years of arduous toil to discover a way of correlating the sense data his brain receives when, for long hours, he gazes at the dials of a highly sophisticated instrument—as if research of this kind could possibly be important! Nor will he feel much inclination to solve a problem when he knows that if he succeeds two problems will arise where there was only one before. He may do it to earn a living—but are there not more worth-while pursuits? He may do it if he is on a "good line" and expects to be credited with a world-renowned "break-through", but will this inspire the rank and file?

In the end the new outlook recoils upon science itself. A striking feature of the educational scene in England is the relative decline of science. Until recently those choosing to take science to A-level standard increased more rapidly than those who chose arts subjects, but after 1963 the trend reversed. In the universities, the Robbins' report envisaged an equal expansion for both science and arts but it seems that there will not now be enough science applicants to warrant the expansion on the science side, nor enough science students wishing to teach the next generation.

The fall, due to the decline in the enchantment which science holds for the adolescent mind, is not confined to England, but is found in the U.S.A. as well. In the pre-1939 era to do research in atomic physics was deemed the pinnacle of success in science, but in a questionnaire a few years back, American teenagers rated "atomic physicist" the least desirable of all in a list of possible careers. A few years before he died Einstein is reported to have said that if he could have his life over again he would not choose science. Oppenheimer's oft-quoted remark to the effect that the atomic scientists had known sin summarizes the view of the ordinary man.

Events are turning out as a Christian would have expected: they must be highly disillusioning for the secularist who was science-intoxicated in the pre-war period.

CHAPTER 6

GOD ON A CLOUD

THE CHURCH-WINDOW GOD

IN EARLIER DAYS, SO IT MIGHT SEEM, MANY CHRISTIANS thought of God as a quasi-material Being. On a stained-glass window you might see Him, as a dignified Monarch with white beard, seated on a cloud-supported throne. Round about is a heavenly host, also cloud-supported, occupied endlessly in chanting songs of praise, while hovering high above the scene might be angels with mighty wings, ever ready to obey the word of command.

The traditional attitude of unbelievers is to regard pictorial representations of this kind with amusement mixed with condescension. The imagery, they claim, is primitive and foolish. Even several centuries ago it was a safe bet that as knowledge increased so the unscientific nature of church-window Christianity would become increasingly manifest.

At first sight this view seems unassailable. The literal-minded atheist can point out that according to science, the universe is not geocentric, so that it is implausible to imagine that the almighty God would remain poised for any length of time above one small planet such as ours. Science makes it impossible any longer to believe that heaven is "up there" in space, or even far away "above the bright blue sky", for—and Russian propaganda is emphatic on the point—astronauts can find no trace of God with His beard. Again, science lends no support to the view that people can sit on clouds without falling through, or the belief that choirs can sing in a vacuum where sound will not carry.

What is the reaction of the Christian? He will agree readily enough that the representations so often used in the past were often unworthy of God, yet he will be less disposed to mock and more disposed to think that the church-window scenes are less stupid than they seem. Perhaps earlier Christianity was trying to express something important. If its symbolism happens to be unpalatable to a modern generation it is of little consequence; what mattered was whether contemporaries for whom it was created understood. The sceptic is altogether too literalistic in his approach; proceed in such a way and not only church windows but symbolic representations in modern art will likewise have to be condemned! Finally, it is mere foolishness to suppose that in order to understand the symbolism of a cloud a man must understand the physics of suspended water droplets.

If the problem had been put to the Christian of a few generations ago, he would certainly have gone further. He would have stated firmly that the Bible and nature are the two books of God and that in the last resort they cannot contradict one another. If, then, the Bible uses symbols to help us think of objects outside sensual experience—and much church-window imagery was derived from the Bible—then in the last resort science ought to do the same. So when the time came, if ever it did, for scientists to describe objects which do not affect our senses, they too would have to drop their literalism and speak in symbols.

Logically, then, the nineteenth-century scientist, if he was a Christian, would have expected science to develop in a way which would make Christian symbolism seem less strange. On the other hand, the sceptic of the time regarded science as a highly literalistic mode of thought and undoubtedly expected that it would remain so.

In which direction, then, do modern developments trend?

SYMBOLISM IN SCIENCE

We may start by dispelling a widespread idea. It is often suggested that earlier Christians chose their symbolism in the way they did because they were ignorant of science. This view, however, makes little sense. It does not need modern science to tell us that a throne cannot be safely set in the sky or that clouds afford no physical support.

Why then the physical symbolism? In our own day we are beginning, perhaps, to see the answer to this question. Though modern man has turned aside from the pictorial representations of the past, he is forced, willy nilly, to think in a similar way himself when he wants to solve his problems.

Recently the scientific press contained an account of an investigation on traffic jams.[1] The Movement of traffic on a modern highway cannot literally be said to be other than it is—movement of traffic. But we are told that the investigators chose to think of it in a way drawn from another discipline. It seemed to them that cars moving along a highway might be compared to a gas passing through a tube. A traffic stream is compressible, like a gas. Like all fluids it speeds up when the road narrows and slows when it broadens. If there are several lanes of traffic the fastest are in the centre as in Newtonian fluids. And so on. There are differences to be sure, but within its limits the "model" is a useful aid to thought.

An interesting point turned up in connexion with traffic lights. If a cock in a pipe carrying a fluid is suddenly turned on or off, a pressure wave travels rapidly along the fluid in both directions. Something closely similar to this is observed in the case of traffic; when a stream is halted at one point each car stops behind the one in front with the result that a "wave" travels down the "fluid", followed by another wave as traffic starts again. These ideas were developed and the conclusion reached that a faster traffic flow could be achieved by breaking streams of traffic up into short segments by suitable timing of traffic lights—a valuable conclusion reached in an unusual way.

The traffic-fluid analogy is but one example of a tendency which is characteristic of investigations in nearly every field of science at the present time. It has been found repeatedly that no progress is possible until scientists let their minds jump right out of one discipline into another. How is an atom constructed? The analogy of the solar system at once suggested itself and was developed mathematically in the early days. What is the atomic nucleus like? Two analogies are used, both successful as far as they go—it may resemble a drop of liquid (with the particles in close contact) or a small ball of gas (in which the particles collide only occasionally). Less prosaic analogies are also freely used—for example Russian atomic physicists speak of particles dressed in "fur coats"![2] How do atoms join together? We imagine negative electricity as a cloud-like formation near an atom which bulges out and overlaps

[1] *New Scientist*, 2 May 1965, p. 263.
[2] A. A. Sokolov, *Elementary Particles*, 1964, writing of the "naked electron" says that it "dresses in an electron-positron fur coat"!

another cloud belonging to a second atom. What about living organisms? "Models" are taken freely from physics and chemistry. Nerves are compared to wires carrying electric currents, the brain to a computer, and the chromosome to a library with a device for finding and opening a particular book at the right page so that a cell will be manufactured of the kind appropriate to its position in the body—part of a hand, eye, heart, etc.

The communication engineer thinks of the muddling up of weak signals which carry messages: to these he applies the law of entropy which originated from the study of steam engines—just as a disordering process in nature makes the energy contained in heat less available for doing useful work, so the muddling up of signals with noise makes the message less and less readable. The idea of entropy, or randomness, has also been usefully applied to decision making, the structure of alloys, the perception of smells, the stretching of rubber, and so on.

CROSS FERTILIZING SYMBOLS

The point will now be clear. If we think about a subject within its own terms of reference, if we confine ourselves to the use of the words and images which properly belong to our field of study, the mind soon grinds to a halt; we go round in circles. As with mathematics, it seems that in the end we can get no more out of our problem than we put in. But then there comes the new insight. Boldly we use ideas and images that are logically quite out of place: our problem lives again.

The alien words and symbols brought in from outside are not literal, but symbolic. The traffic is not a real stream; the entropic change in a complex management decision is not concerned with what the engineer thinks of as real entropy—the entropy of hot steam. The fuzzy surface of a particle is not, literally, a fur coat; the chromosomes in the cells of my body are not, literally, libraries. We talk in symbols: often this is the price we must pay if we would talk at all.

Sometimes, almost unconsciously, we make use of a trick to avoid admitting this fact. We widen the meaning of a stream until it means everything that flows; of entropy until it includes disorder in dustbins or the firm's accounts as well as in the molecular motion of molecules of steam; of a library until it includes a store of information of any kind whatever. In this way, to a limited extent, we may disguise the symbolic nature of our language. But we cannot always do this convincingly, nor can we disguise the fact that when the words were first used outside their usual connotation they were symbolic.

So we are learning slowly that knowledge cannot exist without symbols. The old idea, so beloved of the sceptic, that science would bring us down to some kind of bedrock truth, quite literal and symbol-free, has gone for good. Instead we must choose symbols, models, to bring out, or to emphasize, the points we wish to study. We are not unduly concerned today even if the symbols we choose are not self-consistent—provided they fulfil their function. Sometimes it is useful to think of light or matter as a wave motion, sometimes as a particle; or the nucleus of an atom sometimes as a liquid, sometimes as a gas. Man's use of symbols in science has followed a pattern not far removed from Christian expectation.

RELIGIOUS SYMBOLISM

In this way we begin to see some kind of an answer to the problem with which we started. If we try to keep theology within its limits, it may soon become dry as bones. We cannot see God and this fact alone makes it impossible for us to think of Him in His own terms—divorced from the world of the senses. God, without any picture whatever in the mind, becomes abstract, lifeless and in the end spiritually deadening. Within the private worlds of each of us we make Him live when we allow our thoughts of Him to mingle with our thoughts of the created world. We need thoughts of good men if we would gain a vivid sense of One who is better than all men; we need visions of powerful men or of the gigantic powers of nature if we would think of God who is more powerful than all; we need beautiful sights—sunsets, natural scenery, music —if we would realize that God is beautiful and holy. When men pray they commonly do so with eyes shut so that they may forget the world of the senses, but it is worth remembering that when Jesus prayed He did so with eyes wide open, gazing at the expanse of heaven.

As in science, our symbols may not always be self-consistent. To the Christian, Christ is both the householder with slaves and the servant of all; both the lion and the harmless lamb. Christians themselves are thought of as humble slaves and as the heavenly bride. The symbols may be irreconcilable, but not more so than those of science. Irreconcilability is the reminder that there are limitations to our thinking—a fact which Christians never doubted but scientists have discovered only comparatively recently.

But we must return to our starting point. What is the point of the throne in the sky? Why the clouds as a means of support? The imagery seems odd to a modern age.

The symbolism is clear enough in outline. Early Christians had a vision of the future which we have lost today. The Man on the cloud was the Ruler of earth and heaven. From His vantage point He could see and control everything that exists. With Him were the heavenly host—patriarchs, apostles, martyrs—the faithful of every age. They too would share in their Lord's dominion. The music and the singing symbolized deliberate, unhurried, harmonious action. On the earth below man-made chaos reigned supreme but, unhurried, the all-conquering Christ is working out His purposes.

These symbols are as relevant today as in the past. Why then do we count them strange? The answer is not to be found in our recently won knowledge of the troposphere or of the physics of clouds, but in the fact that we have lost the sense of the reality of the world to come. For most of us today, even among those who call themselves Christians, earth is no longer a testing ground for the glory that shall be hereafter—the partaking with the living Christ in His universal power—but has become an end in itself. If we could but recapture the meaning of *that* Christianity we should find its symbolism meaningful too.

We started by asking how the nineteenth-century atheist and Christian, respectively, might have expected human thought to develop in so far as it related to the use of Christian symbolism. The one, we thought, would have predicted that it would appear in an increasingly unfavourable light as science advanced; the other that it would fall into line with a pattern of ordinary thinking which could not indefinitely be kept out of science itself.

And the outcome? No matter what our opinions, we can hardly resist the conclusion that symbolism is now firmly established in science. Today, no one *on scientific* grounds would wish to resurrect the old objections against Christian symbolism. Events have turned out very much as a Christian might have anticipated.

CHAPTER 7

HELPING THE WEAK

S OME DISEASES AND MANY DEFORMITIES ARE HANDED
down from generation to generation both in human and
animal societies. Farmers who rear livestock can eradicate
undesirable hereditary traits easily enough—animals are killed or
prevented from breeding. But what can be done in a human
society?

KILL THE WEAK?

When this question is raised those who do not feel themselves
bound by the Christian code of ethics often propose an easy
solution. Why not sterilize or kill off those with inherited deformities or diseases, so that these cannot be handed on to succeeding
generations? Would not this be kinder to humanity in the long
run?

In the past, especially in the nineteenth century, this issue often
led to a violent clash between Christianity and science. Whymper,
the famous mountaineer, noting how the valley of Aosta swarmed
with cretins—unhappy beings "punished for the errors of their
fathers"—was horrified to find the Church legalizing marriages
between them. "There is something horribly grotesque," he
wrote, "in the idea of solemnizing the union of a brace of idiots;
and since it is well-known that the disease is hereditary, and
develops in successive generations, the fact that such marriages
are sanctified is scandalous and infamous."[1]

The desire to improve the race by the ruthless application of
scientific methods led many atheists—Nietzsche being the best

---

[1] Edward Whymper, *Scrambles amongst the Alps in the Years 1860–69*; 1871,
p. 308. The passage is omitted in the last (6th; 1936) edition. For the history
of goitre and cretinism, see Sir Humphrey Rolleston's, *The Endocrine Organs*,
1936. The hereditary nature of cretinism was repeatedly confirmed before the
true cause was known.

known—to a violent repudiation of Christianity. Nietzsche taught that we should show kindness only to those who are sound of limb and physically and mentally desirable. To assist the weak and misshapen, to allow the better specimens of humanity to sacrifice themselves for the sake of the feeble and sickly, was, for him, the ultimate sin. No right-minded gardener applies the Golden Rule to slugs and weeds—should decent men behave otherwise towards the weeds of humanity?

In the first flush of Darwinian science, in the nineteenth century, it seemed to many that this issue presented a clear-cut clash between religion and science. The scientists wanted to improve the human stock: the Christians to nurse the weakling and care for the underdog. The laws of nature, working through natural selection, favoured the fit: religion smiled upon the unfit. It was as simple as that. The lessons to be learned from science seemed unambiguous and further progress in the sciences was certain to provide stronger and yet stronger arguments for the extermination of the weak.

CHRISTIAN SUSPICIONS

Many Christians, Darwin's old friend Adam Sedgwick among them, sensed correctly what the effects of the new science would be. They saw it as a danger to mankind, an influence that would lead men away from the Christian teaching of love and respect for others and stir up hatred and strife over the face of the earth. The popularization of the new doctrine could only end in disaster.

Whatever the rights and wrongs of the evolution controversy may have been, there is no doubt that these Christian suspicions were soundly based. Darwinian doctrines of struggle inspired those—Marx, Nietzsche, Hitler, Mussolini, Mao and many others —who destroyed the stability of our world. Though it is certainly possible to reconcile Christianity with evolution—as Charles Kingsley, Asa Gray, Henry Drummond and many others saw even from the early days—this was not how evolution was presented. Rather it depicted nature as the scene of a fierce and ugly struggle in which man himself was now invited to join. Many Christians naturally thought that science had taken a wrong turn: properly interpreted it could not really support the doctrines of social

Darwinism. Throughout the period‧ Christians said, and said repeatedly, that true science and true religion could not be at variance. This formula was the expression of a belief that, in the end, science would validate the Christian way of life.

Thanks to Christian influence Darwinism was partly held in check, just as, in the preceding period, dangerous scientific theories of racism had likewise been vigorously opposed by Christian opinion.[1] Religious objections to evolution, even when Christians had their facts wrong, were immensely valuable in curbing the extravagances of the scientism of the day. Nevertheless, in the name of science, wars of extermination against "inferior" races were waged and justified—a legacy of thought which later influenced Hitler to kill Jews and gypsies and one which is still used, even today, in support of segregation in America.[2] On the social front, afflicted children and the blind and deaf of all ages were sufferers, and there was a serious fall in the number of asylums in England in the second half of the nineteenth century.[3]

Here, as in other cases we have studied, we may discern a clear distinction between the expectations of the atheist on the one hand, and those of the Christian on the other, in regard to the future progress of science. To the nineteenth-century atheist it seemed likely that science would justify increasing ruthlessness;[4] but

---

[1] In the first half of the century the American School of Ethnology upheld slavery with its theory of the multiple origins of man. Though nearly every American naturalist supported this theory, the proffered assistance was rejected by the South *on biblical grounds*. W. Stanton, *The Leopard's Spots: Scientific Attitudes towards Racism in America, 1815–59* (Univ. of Chicago Pr.), 1960, p. 196.

[2] Professor Carlton Coon (*The History of Man,* 1955; *The Origin of Races,* 1963) maintains that there are five races of man, *homo,* some of which have only just evolved past the *sapiens* boundary. Though Coon himself claims that the superiority of the white races is not mental but visceral, i.e. it lies in resistance to disease, his books occasion bitter controversy (see *Nature,* vol. 200, p. 1033, 1963) in the Southern States of America since they are used by many to prove the inferiority of the blacks.

[3] See especially K. W. Hodgson, *The Deaf and their Problems,* 1953, p. 188.

[4] Occasionally, humanitarians (such as T. H. Huxley, in his Romanes Lecture, *Evolution and Ethics,* 1894) argue that man's duty is to *fight* nature. This loophole is hardly open to the Christian who believes that nature is the creation of God.

Christians believed that in the end discovery would show that the Christian moral code was right after all, or if it failed to do just that, it would certainly reveal the fallacy in social Darwinism. What, then, has been the course of subsequent discovery?

LATER DEVELOPMENTS

Firstly, medical research has shown that many apparently hereditary diseases are due to causes which can be remedied, so that the violent methods of the farmyard are unnecessary in the case of man. Today we can afford to smile at the idea that the Swiss should be discouraged from reproducing their kind—for the goitre from which they used to suffer so greatly was due to lack of iodine which is scarce in inland mountainous regions. The deficiency is easily remedied. More intractable diseases are known, of course, but medical science can do much to help the sufferers. In the old days a diabetic lived a miserable existence, suffering great mental depression and loss of strength until he was relieved by an untimely death, but today he lives a relatively normal life. Many other hereditary diseases have been conquered or alleviated and science is not standing still. In view of the amazing progress that has been made the old argument that sufferers should be allowed to die loses its force.

On the biological side, the picture of struggle which emerged from the early Darwinian conceptions is now seen to be grossly exaggerated. By the turn of the century Prince Kropotkin had published his famous book, *Mutual Aid a Factor in Evolution* (1902) in which he showed that co-operation plays at least as large a part in nature as competition.

In more recent years much thought has been given to the problem of what is meant by "the fittest" in the expression "the survival of the fittest". In a civilized society fitness is not measured by fighting, but rather by service to the community. A brilliant inventor or musician may suffer from physical handicaps which would make it impossible for him to survive in a free-for-all struggle, but his presence in the community is of great value. In this sense a physical weakling may be fitter to survive than a dull but physically strong individual.

SICKLE CELLS

In the last decade or so quite a new light has been shed on the problem, particularly in connexion with the disease *sickle cell anaemia*.[1] This is a hereditary disease, handed down through the male or female line, in which some of the blood corpuscles, instead of having their usual saucer-like shape, have instead a distorted appearance rather like that of a sickle. These red blood cells are much less effective oxygen carriers than normal cells, but provided normal cells are also present the disease causes no great inconvenience though there may be shortage of breath. However, if two people marry both of whom have sickle cells, one quarter of the children will have sickle cells only and will die young.

Fortunately, the disease is extremely rare in Britain. It is, however, quite common in some places, notably in parts of Africa and in Cyprus. And where it is common, the chances that two people who both have the condition will marry is greatly increased. Nothing can be done about the disease, but it could certainly be eliminated if all the people who have it were prevented from marrying.

This is the kind of situation which appeals to the eugenist. Here are people who appear to be definitely "unfit", and they are allowed to have children of whom the same is also true. Would it not be wise to rid a country of the disease once and for all for the sake of future generations?

Today we view the situation differently. Scientists have been asking why it is that this particular disease is so widespread in some parts of the world but not in others. It has been discovered that the disease is prevalent where there is malaria and that people with sickle cells in their blood are less afflicted by malaria than others. The disadvantage of having sickle cells is offset by the advantage of not suffering so greatly from malaria. In every country a few people, by a mutation, have sickle cell blood, though the proportion is very low—perhaps one in a million or so. But when the disease confers a decided advantage, then after a few generations the number of cases increases to become a con-

[1] See A. G. Knudson, *Genetics and Disease,* 1965; UNESCO (Symposium), *Abnormal Haemoglobins in Africa,* 1965; CIBA Symposium on *Genetics and Disease,* 1965.

siderable fraction of the whole. If measures were taken to eliminate sickle cell, say in Cyprus, it would therefore eventually return. In the long run nothing would be achieved. On the other hand malaria (if it were not otherwise controlled) would for a time prove more damaging.

The story of sickle cell anaemia illustrates an important principle. If individuals are all exactly alike, then they will all suffer from a disease in the same way. And this approaches what used to happen in past centuries when the weak and sick were uncared-for and when populations mixed less than they do today so that there was much inbreeding. This is how we account for the disastrous effects of imported diseases about which we read in history books. The Black Death decimated the population. At the time of the Spanish conquest of Peru one of the adventurers who went with Cortez developed smallpox and this killed three-quarters of the Incas. When white men settled in the North American continent, most of the natives died of smallpox. In many instances also, entire tribes died out as a result of tuberculosis and venereal diseases. Again, the First World War revealed wide differences in susceptibility to tuberculosis among troops of different nationalities. It is also well known that people with different blood groups may be differently affected by venereal diseases.

Similar phenomena are well known in the animal world. There are marked differences between different cattle breeds in their resistances to some diseases (notably trypanosomiasis). Myxomatosis killed nearly all rabbits in Australia and England, but in its country of origin rabbits were immune.[1] Those who rear livestock are only too familiar with diseases which attack almost every animal of a particular kind on a farm and can be controlled only by slaughtering all those infected. But if diseases are left to run their course there are usually a few individuals which are immune or recover because they have suffered from only a mild attack—the reason being that they are different in some way.

EUGENICS APPLIED

Now let us suppose that the extreme eugenists of the past had been allowed to treat men like animals. They would, of course, have

[1] F. Fenner and F. N. Ratcliffe, *Myxomatosis,* 1965.

selected man for physical and perhaps mental qualities, so that we of today, or perhaps those of a future generation, would be paragons of humanity. Our hospitals would be empty, let us suppose, and congenital diseases would be things of the past. All would go well until some new strain of disease—perhaps a new influenza virus—was introduced into the country. Then it would be a case of the Black Death or worse, all over again.

We now realize that the dreadful sufferings of the Middle Ages were made possible in part by the fact that former generations, without knowing it, did practice a kind of eugenics. When food was short, it was reserved for those who could work in the fields to ensure a crop for the following year; the weak and physically handicapped died. Food condemned as unfit for consumption was sent to hospitals and asylums or given to the lepers, who eventually died out.

After many generations a fairly uniform society was produced, selected on the basic of physical health and strength, but extremely liable to succumb to disease.

HELPING THE WEAK PAYS OFF

Application of the Christian principle that the strong and healthy should be willing to sacrifice themselves for the weak and unfortunate has doubtless done something towards reducing the stamina of the race. Much of this sacrifice has of course taken place in war when men have bravely given their lives for what they thought was right and so helped to preserve the less physically strong who stayed at home—and intermarriage between races, made possible by easy travel is also an important factor. But however it has come about, the willingness of Christians to apply Christian principles of helping and preserving the weak, the sick, and the physically handicapped has helped to produce a society in which there is an extremely complex mixture of human types. So epidemic diseases are held at bay, for we now differ so much that no one disease introduced into our midst is likely to affect us all in the same way. But for this factor we might not be here at all—for modern communications ensure that new diseases reach us from foreign countries at so high a rate that no conceivable medical service could control them. It was difficult enough to ensure man's continuity in the Middle Ages when travel was restricted.

Once again, then, the outcome of research has been to vindicate the faith of the Christian. To the sceptics of yesterday it seemed that the Sermon on the Mount, if followed seriously, would lead to genicide. We now realize that science points the other way; it is not Christian morals but the morals of the over-enthusiastic atheist which might cause disaster.[1]

[1] It might be thought that such atheists are extinct. This is far from so— A. M. Ludovici, in his *Religion for Infidels*, 1961, repeats all the arguments of Nietzsche, and warns mankind of impending disaster unless the weak are left to fend for themselves. Similarly, on the Continent, Nazism is by no means dead.

CHAPTER 8

VARIETIES OF MATTER

THE STORY OF MAN'S ATTEMPTS TO FATHOM THE nature of matter is familiar enough. The theory of the four elements—earth, air, fire and water—was early on the scene, as was also the notion that all material things are made of water, which was supposed to be capable of appearing in limitless guises. But reliable knowledge, squarely based on experiment, did not begin till the early part of the nineteenth century with Dalton's atomic theory. It then became clear that matter consists of very small particles of different kinds which cannot normally be further divided or transformed into one another. These particles, called *atoms*, merely change places in chemical transformations, so giving rise to the astonishing variety of material things that we see around us.

In the period from about 1860 onwards it was noticed that the different kinds of atoms, about a hundred in number, fall into families, which suggests that they are built according to a plan—an idea associated with the names of Newlands, Mendeléeff and others.

At first this suggestion encountered opposition, for experiment seemed to point in the opposite direction. In particular, the chemist Stas, after a lifetime of work, showed that some of the weights of the atoms are fractional, which was not to be expected if all were built out of the simplest unit, that of hydrogen, but the explanation for this was not discovered until many years later. Meanwhile, however, the discovery that elements could be grouped together in a convincing way—so convincing that the properties of unknown elements were successfully predicted—had come to stay. And with the gradual discovery of the missing elements it seemed that the end of physical and chemical science was well in sight. Before many years had passed the roll-call would be complete. No other kinds of matter were conceivable. Man would have sampled the universe.

LITTLE TO DISCOVER

But perhaps there was just a chance that some hidden mystery still remained to be discovered. While the atoms were rushing to and fro in their eternal dance, while they were combining in wonderful ways and breaking apart again—was there just a possibility, perhaps , that a few new ones might arise, or a few disappear? . . . Something to bring an element of excitement and change into nature, something to relieve the drabness of eternal ever-cycling aeons and tempt the scientist to burn his midnight oil?

Chemist after chemist worked at the problem, each using the utmost refinements of the technology of his day. Is it possible, these men wondered, to detect a small change in weight when atoms combine, or when they fall apart? But the results were always the same—negative. The change, if there was one, was beyond the capacity of science to detect—less than one part in a million (later revised to a hundred million). Matter was eternal after all! It did not change from age to age. Atoms rushed this way and that participating in multitudinous adventures; they made new groupings, they broke apart, they cascaded off to new liaisons; but never did they change a whit. At the end every one was there as on creation's morning: and their weights were what they had always been.

It was a picture well suited to the materialistic temper of the day—the latter part of the nineteenth century. Physicists were beginning to feel that they would soon be out of a job. They began to lament among themselves that the only task left for them to do was to find the constants of nature to another place of decimals. And at that time it was not clear that even this was important. Such was the prevailing mood. But at least one devout Christian, James Clerk Maxwell, would have none of it. Near the end of the road? "We have no right to think thus of the unsearchable riches of creation," he said in his inaugural lecture when he was appointed to the Professorship of physics at Cambridge (1871). How right he was!

The years which followed brought one startling discovery after another. Radio waves, X-rays, the electron, the quantum theory, radio-activity, the structure of the atom—with many more to follow. The old dogmatisms had gone. Nature was vastly more complex than had been supposed. Physicists had never been busier.

THE MODERN ERA

By the end of the 1920's things were settling down again. A new simplicity seemed on the way—at least for those who could shut their eyes to the more disconcerting discoveries that had been reported. The universe was made of electricity. It contained only negative and positive charges. Given space and electric charges, the chemical elements would form automatically and their properties would follow as a matter of course. Nature was so simple that, perhaps, it obeyed just one simple equation and, when man had found it, the days of mystery would be ended.

The picture satisfied materialists well enough, but not Christians. It seemed to offer little scope for a creative God, let alone the possibility of free-will or miracle. Was it not obvious, from a Christian standpoint, that science had scarcely started on her quest? The writer can remember vividly how, as a schoolboy in the early twenties, he once said to himself in effect, "Well, if that is true, it will make it harder to believe in God. But of course it can't be true!" Nor was it.

Once again there followed, in the thirties, a welter of new discoveries and they have come thick and fast ever since. Though we cannot as yet, with any certainty, link them with Christianity, it can hardly be questioned that the general tenor of discovery falls into line with Christian expectations.

STRANGE MATTER

It has always been held by Christians (as by those of other faiths) that unfamiliar forms of matter exist. For instance, after Jesus had risen from the dead, He appeared to His disciples. To a casual onlooker He seemed normal—He was mistaken both for a gardener and for a stranger in Jerusalem. He could be touched, could handle ordinary physical objects, could speak in a normal way and exhibit mannerisms which He had had before His death— indeed His disciples recognized Him by the way he broke bread. But His powers were also beyond anything which we associate with the atoms out of which an ordinary human body is made. He could appear and disappear at will and could pass through ordinary matter—for example locked doors. There are also other stories in the Bible which have many points in common with that of Jesus after His resurrection.

If we take these stories at their face value, then the universe contains (or at least sometimes contains) varieties of "matter" other than the ordinary matter with which we are familiar. On the one hand it may feel physical to the touch and it must reflect light like ordinary matter, for otherwise it would not be visible. In several instances it is described as brilliantly luminescent. It must therefore be capable of reacting with ordinary electromagnetic waves, both absorbing, emitting and reflecting like ordinary matter. On the other hand as we have just seen it differs from ordinary matter through which it can pass without restriction, it is unaffected by gravitation and temperature, and most important of all it is directly under the control of mind.

Can more be said? Perhaps. A physicist might argue that the new kind of matter cannot contain electric charges, otherwise it would not be capable of passing freely through ordinary matter. But since its texture is extremely like that of ordinary matter, it might well be constructed according to the same plan, but with some force other than electromagnetic force holding atoms together. Or just possibly it might be a kind of matter in which both masses and charges are vastly smaller than those with which we are familiar but otherwise related in the same way, so that its "atoms" can combine to form molecules.

MERE SPECULATION!

To many, of course, all that we have been saying will seem irresponsibly speculative. After all, miracles are not everyday affairs. And why should we expect them, or anything connected with them, to be capable of discovery by science?

This objection may arise from disbelief that the miracles ever took place as recorded—which is fair enough—but for the moment we are asking how a serious-minded Christian who *does* believe in the miracles might expect science to develop. But it *may* also arise from a feeling that there is something wrong, something irreverent, in supposing that miracles can be brought within the ambit of scientific research. If such a "stuff" exists, why should we expect to discover it by the methods of science? Would it not be wholly under the influence of God? Perhaps, though we cannot be sure.

A natural view to take is that God makes use of what He has already created. Just as ordinary life makes use of the atoms of chemistry to build material bodies, so spiritual beings may make use of "material" of another kind which already exists in the universe. But if we are right in thinking this, then physical methods might in the last analysis be capable of telling us something about it, because as we have already noted it can and does react with ordinary physical forces. (We shall return to this theme considered from a rather different point of view, in the following chapter.) Here again, then, we see that Christianity leads us to expect science to develop in a certain way.

We conclude that in the field of physical science, we should expect the Christian to be more open to discovery of new forces than is the atheist. The Christian is reasonably certain that the present state of knowledge is incomplete and this encourages him to think along new lines. The traditional agnostic, on the other hand, tends to be content with what is already known and so is more determined to fit all facts into the procrustean bed of present-day knowledge. Disbelieving in the miracles, he has no need to think that present ideas, if explored far enough, will fail in any foreseeable direction.

RECENT DEVELOPMENTS

How far, then, have Christian expectations been fulfilled? We have now progressed a long way since the early part of the century when it was supposed that there were only two kinds of matter—electrons and protons.

First came the neutron, then the positron, then particles with weights in between those of electrons and protons (mesons) or greater than protons (baryons). There are neutrinos too, which are either massless or much lighter than electrons. Charges on all the particles may be zero, positive or negative. For a time it seemed that the total number might be around 30–40 but more recently it increased again and passed the 100 mark. Many of the "fundamental" particles seem to be formed from others which can have different energy states. Physicists are now at the beginning of an attempt to bring them together, classifying them into groups with a view to learning how they are related.

It is clear that many different new kinds of matter can exist and small quantities of some of them have been made. The simplest is *anti-matter* which is like ordinary matter but has the charges reversed—it has a heavy negative core but positive electrons on the outside. All the elements and perhaps the whole of chemistry could be duplicated in anti-matter but it cannot exist on earth (except in vacuum tubes for an exceedingly short time) for when it comes into contact with ordinary matter it instantly explodes. According to the latest evidence anti-matter is not, as previously thought, precisely the same as matter but with the charges reversed: a physicist, suddenly projected into a world of *either* matter or anti-matter would be able to discover which it was.

There are other kinds of matter theoretically possible, in which the centres of the atoms consist of various kinds of mesons or baryons, suitably charged, with oppositely charged lighter particles rotating round them. It is possible that all forms of ordinary matter might be duplicated by some of them.

Many of the newly discovered particles are unstable in the free state. But we must remember that the neutron, too, is unstable when free, decomposing with a half-life of about twenty minutes, yet when combined in the nucleus of an atom it is permanently stable. So it does not follow that because so many particles are unstable they could not become stable when suitably combined in some new kind of matter.

The neutrino is a particularly interesting particle. Neutrinos, which are of two kinds, have no detectable charge or mass—it is thought, however, that they must have an exceedingly small mass, much smaller than that of the electron. They are unaffected by gravity and pass freely through other forms of matter. They are plentiful in nature—in fact a sizeable proportion of the energy of stars is given out in the form of neutrinos—about 10 per cent in the case of the sun. At present neutrinos are still extremely difficult to detect but if ever it becomes possible to construct a neutrino telescope it will be possible to see deep down into the interior of the sun and perhaps of the earth and planets too.

At present we cannot make neutrinos interact with electro-magnetic forces except very rarely, but perhaps they may do so more easily under the right conditions; or there may be other equally elusive particles to be discovered in years to come.

In conclusion, no one would claim that "spiritual matter" has been discovered by science. But the pointer of discovery is certainly set in a direction which is no cause for surprise to the Christian, whereas atheists and agnostics have often been satisfied with limited horizons.

CHAPTER 9

HALF-WAY SUBSTANCE?

TWO KINDS OF STUFF

I N THE LAST CHAPTER WE CONSIDERED THE POSSIBILITY
that nature contains materials which spiritual beings use in
order to perform "miracles".

At the back of these speculations is the idea—an idea which
Christianity shares with most other religions—that there are two, or
at least two, different kinds of "stuff" in the universe. Christians
express this belief, often called *dualism*, when they insist that there
is a real distinction between the natural and the supernatural; the
material and the spiritual; the corporeal and the incorporeal or (as
St. Paul puts it in 1 *Corinthians*, 15) the earthy and the heavenly.
However, the distinction is often questioned and atheist philoso-
phers argued that it is false. How then does the subject stand today and what light can science shed upon it?

Let us start with the philosophical difficulty. If it is true—so the
argument goes—that there are two different kinds of reality, two
different sorts of "stuff" which have nothing in common, it
follows that they cannot influence each other. If it is found that
what we assume to be such realities *do* in fact influence each other,
this proves that they have something in common after all, so that
they are not really two but one. Religious people, it is said, try to
hold two mutually inconsistent beliefs at the same time. They
want their dualism, but they also want their realms of spirit and of
matter to interact with one another. They believe in a soul
immaterial enough to survive death; yet they say that the soul acts
upon the body and the body on the soul. Glorious inconsistency!

From this statement of the case it is easy to conclude that the
universe must be monistic after all—that ultimately only one kind
of "stuff" exists.

But what kind of "stuff" might it be? There are three possible
answers: the "stuff" might be matter (*materialism*); or mind
(*idealism* or *spiritualism*—not to be confused with the sect which

seeks to make contact with the dead!); or it might lie somewhere between these extremes as in the doctrine that elementary particles are small self-conscious creatures or *monads* which are both material and spiritual in nature (*monadology*). However we shall say no more here about these theories because no thinking Christian is likely to take them seriously and, as we shall see, the philosophical argument for monism is quite unconvincing.

HOW CAN SPIRIT INFLUENCE MATTER?

Let us return to our starting point. The Christian is unimpressed by philosophical and verbal arguments which purport to prove that the spiritual and the material cannot influence one another;[1] he starts with the premise that they are essentially different, yet they *do* interact.

But *how* can it happen? The answer is quite simple. If two realities of different kinds cannot react upon one another *directly*, they may yet do so indirectly. This suggestion which is very old, led to the belief that God must have created an intermediate kind of reality or "stuff" which has something in common with material things on the one hand and with mind or spiritual reality on the other. According to this view the material and spiritual realms are themselves distinct but each can influence or be influenced by the intermediate "stuff". We may liken the new "stuff" to an interpreter: two people wish to converse but neither knows a word of the other's language; the interpreter understands them both and makes conversation possible.

THE HUNT FOR THE GO-BETWEEN

What then is the intermediate stuff and where may it be found? Many of the earlier suggestions failed because the intermediates suggested were either not material enough or too material: so they were not genuine intermediates at all.

---

[1] Far less in claiming that they do not interact at all, but only appear to do so—as in the celebrated doctrine known as *occasionalism* (Malebranche), according to which the appearance is due to a pre-established harmony—reality being like two clocks wound up at the beginning of time, but never getting out of step.

Thus Galen, the ancient anatomist, invented the theory of animal spirits. This mysterious substance, apparently wholly spiritual in nature, travelled through supposedly hollow nerves from one part of the body—the heart or the brain—to the muscles, causing them to move according to the dictates of the will. And conversely, feeling was explained by saying that the animal spirits returned from the sense organs to the seat of consciousness. On this view, held until a few centuries ago, animal spirits constituted the intermediate stuff. It was "the soul's Vehicle and Habit", and at death, so it was thought, it left the body, becoming diffused through the "great aetherial Ocean . . . ready to be united to the Soul at the instant of his Separation."[1]

Another belief, widely held in the seventeenth century and probably handed down from the Middle Ages, was that the soul itself was the intermediate stuff. Spirit and matter had nothing in common, but both had affinity with the soul. A rather similar idea (due to Ralf Cudworth,[2] the Cambridge Platonist) was that God had created a special omnipresent material called "plastic nature" —"a sort of middle substance between matter and spirit" as Disraeli discribes it[3]. As with animal spirits and the soul, it was not possible to detect plastic nature by the senses or even to describe it in an intelligible way.

These supposed intermediates had none of the properties of matter, for they could not be detected by the methods of science. What was needed was a quasi-material object or stuff—a genuine intermediate.

Fernel put forward a new suggestion—later immortalized by René Descartes. The anatomists of the day had said, it later turned out wrongly, that man differs from beast in possessing a pineal gland. So the suggestion was diffidently made that the soul lived in this gland and the gland itself had the properties of the half-way stuff—it was acted on by both the soul and the body and could in turn act upon each of them.

Now it was not necessary, in principle, to identify the organ in the human body which played this wonderful role, so many were content to speak of the *sensorium*, "the seat of the sensation in the

[1] Henry Power, *Experimental Philosophy*, 1664.
[2] *The Intellectual System of the Universe*, 1678.
[3] I. D'Israeli, *Amenities of Literature*, 1841, p. 719.

brain . . . the percipient centre to which sense-impressions are transmitted by the nerves" (O.E.D.) and to hold with Power that the soul also acts on the sensorium when it wishes to activate the muscles.

Historically, we owe at least one of the truly great discoveries of science to reasoning of this kind—albeit in a more sophisticated form.[1] In the sixteenth century van Helmont, convinced that an intermediate kind of material must exist, set out to find it. As a result he discovered *gases*: today his name is immortalized as the discoverer of carbon dioxide or "gas of the wild woods" as he pleased to call it. Van Helmont also became acquainted with other gases in various states of purity, particularly carbon monoxide and nitrous oxide. He believed that gases were neither material nor spiritual but partook of both natures at the same time so that they established a link between the two. Nevertheless he did not think of himself as an out-and-out dualist.

Today it is plain that van Helmont did not find the material for which he was looking. On cooling all gases turn into liquids or solids, which resemble other forms of matter; conversely many forms of matter vaporize on heating. So there is nothing special about gases: they belong to the realm of matter. Fernel, Descartes and van Helmont did not find what they were looking for, but were they looking in the right direction? Can there be a half-way stuff—not gas but something else?

NEWTON'S SUGGESTION

The discovery of the law of gravitation by Newton opened new possibilities. Newton thought it unphilosophical, indeed in the highest degree absurd, to suppose that one piece of matter could act upon another at a distance in the absence of an intermediate material to carry the message. Descartes, Huygens, Leibnitz, in fact all the great thinkers of the day, agreed. Direct action at a distance, said Descartes, implied that all the particles of matter in

[1] W. Pagel, *H. B. van Helmont*, Berlin, 1930; *Bulletin Hist. Instit. Hist. Medicine*, 1935, Vol 3; *Trans. Vict. Instit.*, 1942, 74, 99; *The Religious and Philosophical Aspects of van Helmont's Science and Medicine* (Bulletin of History of Medicine, Suppl. 2) Baltimore 1944. Van Helmont's theology also led him a surprisingly modern "alien ferment" theory of disease.

the universe must be endowed with souls possessed of knowledge "of a truly divine sort, so that they may know without any medium what takes place at very great distances and act accordingly".[1]

Equally perplexing was the fact that a gyroscope (or the plane of swing of a pendulum) faithfully keeps direction in space relative to the fixed stars. How can it unfalteringly know the direction of these stars, when it is on a rotating platform—the earth—and when clouds cover the sky? Can empty nothingness perform such a wonder as this? Newton, with others, especially Robert Boyle, began to suspect that space was connected with God in some special way.

Around 1675 Newton was wondering whether the ether of space was a material substance of some kind "much of the same constitution with air, but far rarer, subtiler and more strongly elastic". If so, he reckoned, and if the ether atoms were of different sizes, then larger ones might get pushed aside by ordinary matter and their efforts to regain their former position might cause gravitational attraction. But he had "little fancy to things of this nature"[2] preferring to leave them to others.

But Newton did not lose interest in space. He continued to discuss the subject with men, like David Gregory,[3] who were not controversially minded—for he hated controversy. By the beginning of the century he was convinced that space was intimately connected with theology and he came to think that it is in fact, the sensorium of the Deity—an idea which may have originated with the Cambridge Platonists. Newton is emphatic, however, that space is *not* God, nor can it be regarded in any way as the *body* of God.[4] In evidence of this he argues that *we* cannot be identified with that part of our brains which interacts with our body, and that no one would claim that this part *is* the same as his body. But if space is God's sensorium, how can He know what happens in the universe seeing that He has no nerves and no organs of sense? Newton's answer to this is that in our bodies the sensorium is a

[1] Quoted by Pierre Duhem, *The Aim and Structure of Physical Theory*, 1954 ed., p. 15. For a summary of the controversies on this subject, see also Alexandre Koyré, *Newtonian Studies*, 1965.

[2] *Letter to Boyle.*

[3] *Principia*, 1713 ed., Scholium Generale.

[4] W. G. Hiscock (Ed.), *David Gregory, Isaac Newton and their Circle*, 1937.

physically small structure, so that we need means whereby messages from the world outside can be brought to this central region. But if events actually took place inside the sensorium, we should need no sense organs at all, for we should be immediately aware of what was happening. And this, according to Newton, is the situation with God. Space is His sensorium, so that He is immediately aware of everything which happens: he has no need of eyes, ears, organs of touch, or nerves.

Just as we can make our muscles contract by sending out messages from a central region, in this way interfering with the way they would behave if left alone, so God can do likewise. He can do it in so-called empty space where He is as free to act in His sensorium as we in ours. In our imagination, in the private world hovering around our sensorium, we also can do what we please, building castles in the air, or turning base metals to gold. We are not obliged to send messages to the outer world unless we so desire. And God's freedom cannot be less than ours. In space, which is His private world, He can do as He pleases. If He wishes He can create matter of the kind familiar to us, but He can make unfamiliar kinds too, "of different densities and forces". In this way He can "vary the laws of nature" and if He so wishes can even "make worlds of several sorts in several parts of the universe". (Newton's amazing speculations often have a modern ring!)

According to Newton, God's sensorium is not confined to "empty" space. Newton was insistent that all matter contains pores, even the densest. In proof of this he elsewhere (in his *Optiks*) cites the case of a gold vessel which was filled with water, closed and squeezed, whereupon water passed through the metal and stood up in little beads on the outside. So there is space, the sensorium of God, everywhere. And however small the pores in matter may be, they cannot squeeze space out. For this space is not made of atoms, but "is divisible *in infinitum*" so that it is present even in the smallest pores. And God is "everywhere present" in His universe and everywhere able to vary nature's laws.

THE PROBLEM TODAY

We have traced the suggestion that there exists an intermediate substance between mind and matter up to the beginning of the eighteenth century, since which time it would appear no further suggestions have been made. How then have these ideas fared since then?

For the materialist, of course, there is no problem. No intermediate material is required. Man's mind will in time penetrate into the depths of nature and all the supposed intermediates will disappear by absorption into science, like van Helmont's gases. Christians, on the other hand, though recognizing that wrong identifications of the intermediate stuff have been made, have often supposed that such a stuff exists.

There are two problems involved here, one concerning man and his relationship to his body, the other God and His relationship to the world.

Firstly, then, is there any evidence today of a sensorium in the human brain? Perhaps there is. Though the suggestion that the pineal gland is the seat of the soul has long been held to ridicule, T. H. Thorpe reminds us that the recent discovery of a centre of consciousness at the base of the brain, in the brain stem, might well be interpreted as a seat of the soul.[1] If this small area is destroyed an animal enters a perpetual sleep from which it cannot be aroused.

Perhaps a more likely view is that advanced by Eccles[2] according to which the mind "lives" in the dominant hemisphere—that is, in the cortex on the left side for a right-handed person. When the connecting links between the two hemispheres are severed, the two sides of the brain work independently, but there is no indication of a splitting of mental unity. The right side of the brain then works simply as a computer. The left hand (controlled by the right side of the brain) can handle an object, find it among other objects, even learn about it in a simple way, but the "I" cannot name the object and (with eyes shut) has no "feel" of what is happening, not even of where the left hand is at the time. On this view the "centre of consciousness" merely bombards the "mind" with stimuli to keep it alert.

These recent and suggestive discoveries make it quite possible

[1] W. H. Thorpe, *Biology, Psychology and Belief* (Eddington Memorial Lecture), 1961, p. 23. See also, *Science, Man and Morals*, 1965.

[2] Sir John Eccles, *The Brain and the Unity of Conscious Experience* (Eddington Memorial Lecture), 1965.

that the mind is, rather literally, a "ghost in a machine". If this is so, then some part of the brain, perhaps the dominant hemisphere, may be regarded as the sensorium.

GOD, NATURE AND ETHER

Turning to the wider problem of the relationship of God to nature, nothing that has been discovered in the intervening years has proved Newton wrong.

Today we are still as much in the dark as he about the nature of gravity. But for Newton this was the only problem; he thought that light consisted of particles, but we now think that the same space which carries gravity also carries light.

Today, as in Newton's time, we cannot accept space as just nothingness. The evidence that the universe contains an ether of some kind piles up steadily. Space has quite definite properties, for it is associated with "fields" of force which have direction. There are gravitational, electromagnetic and other less well-known fields (responsible for the strong and weak interactions in nuclear physics). So far as we know there is no limit to the fineness of their structure, for fields in space do not change in strength or direction in small jerks, as does, say, the strength of an electro-magnet when the current is increased.

Modern theories of matter assume that space contains energy deficiencies or "holes" as well as points where energy is more than zero. Authorities such as Eddington and Dirac have expressed themselves strongly to the effect that there *must* be an ether. A few decades back it was commonly assumed that relativity removed the need to suppose that the ether existed and undergraduates laughingly said that the ether was the noun corresponding to the verb to *undulate*. This view is not tenable.

But still we are faced with questions we cannot answer. Is emptiness or nothingness *filled* with the ether? Can nothingness exist without it? What are the properties of ether? All attempts, covering centuries, to answer these questions have proved abortive. We seem to have reached an intellectual impasse.

The quite astonishing fact is that the universe is made in such a way that it is impossible to measure a single one of the properties of ether. We cannot determine its density, it viscosity, its elasticity, its mass, its energy, its velocity. . . . Indeed, relativity makes nonsense of a physical picture, for the light that travels ahead from the headlamp of a quickly moving car moves no faster than when the car is still. Half a century of carefully conducted experiments have shown beyond doubt that no relative motion between ether and the earth, or any physical body, can be detected.

Is then this space, this space-time (call it what we will) *part* of the material world? It must be so because it reacts with the material world. It carries gravity. Its vibrations bring light from far-away stars and galaxies, keeping frequencies constant to a quite fantastic degree of accuracy over long aeons of time. The forces it transmits hold matter together. Why then is it so elusive? Why can we learn nothing about it by the methods of science? Indeed, why are we forced to build science on foundations which make no mention of it at all?

The answer seems to be that it does not belong to the physical world. It both belongs to the physical world and does not belong. Does it, however, interact with a non-material world of spirit?

Today there is accumulating and fairly convincing evidence that human minds can transmit thought and emotion by non-physical means. In some way ideas are carried through space and interact with a nervous system—and the rules which hold for vibrations (more especially the inverse square law) do not hold here. This suggests that in some very limited way—for we possess the faculty of telepathy only in a primitive form—space can act as an extended sensorium of the human mind. It is concerned not only with physical fields of force (gravitational, electric, magnetic, etc.) which can be measured but with what we may call a field of thought. Ideas of this kind, based on experimental studies, have been advanced by highly educated atheists (e.g., Whateley Carington[1]) in our day and so cannot be explained away as Christian rationalizations. If space is God's sensorium, it is not unreasonable to think that sometimes at least, and to a very limited degree, man who was made in the image of God may share the same sensorium. After all, wherever in his nervous system man's sensorium may be, space is there too.

Perhaps a philosophical system, a kind of Christian idealism, could be built along these lines. Is it because he shares the same

[1] W. W. Carington, *Telepathy*, 1945.

sensorium with God, that the thought-creations of God appear physically real to man? Was Bishop Berkeley right in constructing his universe out of thought—God's thought? We are in deep waters here, but evidence is so hard to come by that the scientifically trained man will generally want to say with Newton that he has "little fancy to things of this nature".

Further evidence (for those who accept the alleged facts) of the direct action of mind on space is afforded by the appearance of ghosts, of poltergeistic movements and—especially interesting to the Christian—many of the miraculous appearances recorded in the Bible. These strange happenings suggest that spiritual beings can make themselves visible—and since light consists of electromagnetic waves in the ether, it may mean that spirit can act upon this medium.

One thing we should like to know is whether mind—our own minds say (or that part of them which survives death)—acts directly on the ether, which in turn actuates the body.

Experiments show that we can, by mere thought, actuate individual nerve fibres in the nervous system.[1] Do we do this by manipulating a field in the ether near by, or do we act directly on the molecules near at hand? In principle it might be possible to find out by experiment, say by implanting minute coils in the nervous system and finding out whether by acts of will it might be possible to generate currents in them too weak to actuate the nerves—the latter might be rendered less sensitive by drugs.

If then, ether or space is the half-way "stuff" between the spiritual and the material, we may imagine that it is acted on and sometimes built up into complex structures from *either* direction. Fields of very great complexity are present in a complicated molecule or crystal but it is possible that such fields could be formed without the associated matter. In fact the usual theory of the electron pictures it as the site of an intense field, but without a particle at the centre. Physicists argue that centres of intense electric fields like this are stable and are, in fact what we call electrons. Can mind create centres of this or some other kind in space,

---

[1] J. V. Basmajian has described fascinating experiments in which "tunes" are played on *individual* neurones which operate *individual* fibres in a small muscle in the hand. (*Science*, 1963, **141**, 440; *New Scientist*, 12 December 1963; See also *Nature*, 1965, **207**, 957 for further references.)

perhaps building them up into complex structures, perhaps causing their annihilation again? If intense points of electric field
make up ordinary matter, may not similar intense points of one of
the other kinds of field known to science constitute matter of
another kind? Need we even be limited to the fields which have
already been discovered by science? A number of lines of evidence,
as Broad shows, indicate that a discarnate mind does have a
"body" of some kind and Broad himself concludes that the best
way of picturing it is to imagine it as built of something like the
nineteenth-century ether.[1] Some such view as this might throw
light not only on existence after death but on ghosts and other
strange phenomena.

All this is suggestive. Can it be that the mysterious "stuff"
which gives what seems like empty space its astonishing properties, is what van Helmont and others were seeking? Was Newton
right in thinking that it is the sensorium of God—the half-way
stuff, the interpreter between the spiritual and the material? Today,
a scientist can still say what Newton said: "At least I see nothing
in contradiction in all this."

Once again, it is fair to conclude that modern science is not
pointing the way the atheist thought it would. He expected a tidy
and simple world with a gradual increase in the power of scientific
understanding so that there would be no room, in the end, for
quasi-material substances to forge a link between matter and a
world which, according to him, does not even exist. Things have
turned out otherwise. Perhaps we have even discovered what it
was that Christians sought for centuries.

[1] C. D. Broad, *Lectures on Psychical Research*, 1962, p. 419. Professor Broad, a
professed atheist, concludes his very careful analysis of the available evidence
relating to the nature of mind, with the words: "We can conceive of a form
of dualism, not inconsistent with the known facts of physics, physiology and
psychology" which would make survival possible (p. 416.)

CHAPTER 10

ATHEISTIC SCIENCE IN RUSSIA

RUSSIAN SCIENCE[1]

I F CHRISTIANITY IS TRUE AND, IN ADDITION, HAS A vested interest in science, it might well be expected that the Christian (or partly Christian) Western world would make fewer scientific mistakes than the professedly atheistic Russians. We might further suppose that mistakes in the East would often be the result of atheistic prejudice.

In considering the development of science since the beginning of the communist régime, we must bear in mind that Russia was—to some extent still is—a very backward nation by Western standards. But the progress that has been achieved against great odds—often involving much suffering—has come, in theory at least, through fanatical determination to use science for the betterment of the people.

In any society, of course, we may expect to encounter eccentric individuals who advance unorthodox opinions. This is a sign of health, for such opinions are sometimes right—and even when they are wrong they not infrequently act as catalytic stimuli which lead to new advances. But from the early days of the communist régime Russian science has been characterized by much needless violent opposition to views which are essentially sound, and recognized as such by the rest of the civilized world. And these perversions have been officially favoured, or enjoyed wide popularity, simply because they seemed to stand in opposition to Christianity and idealistic philosophy, or because atheistic apologists found them useful for propaganda purposes. Moreover,

---

[1] For documented information on Russian attitudes to science and philosophy, see the invaluable journal, *Studies in Soviet Thought* (Dordrecht, Holland, 1961–) Translations of many scientific articles appear in *Current Digest of the Soviet Press*. Information on Russian work in E.S.P. will be found in the *Journal of Parapsychology* for recent years.

it appears that in a remarkably large number of instances the names of highly respected Russian men of science were or are involved.

PHYSICAL SCIENCES

Let us take astronomy first. In the 1930's astronomers in the West came to believe that the universe is expanding and this suggested that there had once been an epoch of creation. The theory of relativity was much used at the time in support of this view. The outlook in astronomy was becoming too favourable for "bourgeois metaphysics", including religion, and Western astronomy was therefore attacked violently in the Soviet Press. The attack reached a climax in 1949 when a number of Russian astronomers holding Western ideas were liquidated. The Soviet Academy officially rejected relativity, together with the "idea of a finite but expanding universe, which Western astronomers regard as a consequence of relativity theory". For a quarter of a century relativity was proscribed in Russia—and after that it was only reinstated when it was officially decided that it did not contradict Marxist theory after all!

Turning to physics—in the early years after the Revolution the new views, due to Einstein, Bohr, Heisenberg and others, did much to change the basic viewpoint of the physicist. A limit was established beyond which the materialistic law of cause and effect could not be traced: statistics and probability replaced the old certainties. These views encouraged idealism among the physicists —or so the Russians thought—and some of the new advances had been made by professedly religious men. The Russian Academy of Science accordingly denounced Einstein, Bohr and Heisenberg as "obscurantist or *bourgeois* metaphysicians". Translations of their philosophical books and those of Eddington were forbidden. In addition statisticians who applied their methods to physical theory were attacked and the use of statistics in biology was curtailed. Even in chemistry, it was feared that the theory of resonance tended towards idealism, so this too was attacked.[1] Russians were reminded that Lenin himself had been greatly troubled by a similar development many years before. In his

[1] *Nature*, 1952, **169**, 92, 860.

writings Lenin "points out with much indignation that the idealist trends in the philosophy of science which were current in the first decade of the present century were accompanied by a recrudescence of theism quite incompatible with . . . Marxism". For Lenin, theism was regarded as "a particularly pernicious form of metaphysics, since it involves not only the acceptance of ideas foreign to dialectical materialism, but also invades the spheres of morality and social behaviour".

BIOLOGY

The best known instance of the effect of atheism on Russian science is in the field of genetics, which suffered greatly until quite recently, with much harm to the Russian economy.

The Marxists refused to accept the reality of the gene, partly because genetics had been started by Mendel who was an ordained priest, and partly because a gene is an invisible body postulated to account for what can be seen in the adult plant or animal—a view which to the hypersensitive mind of atheists is highly idealistic. When a Russian geneticist tried to defend the gene on the ground that it was no more metaphysical than the atom of chemistry, Prezent retorted, "Far closer would be an analogy between the invisible gene and the invisible spirit."[1]

Believers in genes were deprived of their posts, banished, and often allowed to die under the fearful conditions pertaining in the far Eastern prison camps. Amongst students it became as dangerous to possess Western textbooks on genetics as to possess reactionary literature.[2]

[1] *The Situation in Biological Science*, Proc. Lenin Academy of Agricultural Sciences of the U.S.S.R. (Eng. Trans.), Moscow, 1949, p. 602.

[2] See J. S. Huxley, *Soviet Genetics and World Science,* 1949; P. S. Hudson and R. H. Richens, *The New Genetics in the Soviet Union*, School of Agriculture, Cambridge, 1946.

The August issue of *Oktyabr* 1965 contains an interesting account of the history of the genetics controversy by G. Platonov. The author humbly repents for having supported Lysenko in the past. He is chiefly concerned to attack B. M. Kedrov who formerly opposed genes, Weismannism and Western ideas generally because they "turned biology into naked idealism and metaphysics" (Kedrov, 1948) but who now (1965) pretends that all along he has said that the orthodox theory of heredity "is not idealism but genuine materialism"! (Trans., in C.D.S.P. **17**, No. 41, pp. 3–10.)

In biology the origin of life was always a sore point with Marxists. Since the days of Louis Pasteur it has been generally believed that spontaneous generation of life is impossible and this teaching was accepted in Russia as elsewhere. But in homes and schools such a view encouraged children to ask how the first living things arose. This gave Christians the opportunity to say that God was the author of life.

Before the war, A. I. Oparin made some pseudo-scientific guesses about the origin of life in the early ages of the world. These were highly speculative, and in fact based on virtually no solid ground at all save that when organic substances in solution are concentrated they will sometimes separate as little drops (coacervates) which he said were probably the beginnings of living cells. His book was written with the deliberate object of making it unnecessary to believe in God. In the West it might have received little attention but Russian authorities had it translated into the language of every country under their influence and it was circulated in large numbers. This and many similar books attacking religion on supposedly scientific grounds were and still are sent for review to Western countries and every favourable comment is made use of to spread atheism in the East.[1] Needless to say many materialists in the West are favourably disposed towards Oparin's views; but others are candid enough to admit that they are unconvincing[2] and would receive no credence but for the fact that there seems no other alternative to believing in God as creator of life.

FRINGE SCIENCE

In Russia as in other countries constant attempts are made by fringe-scientists to make life in the laboratory—not of course in a

[1] Dr. T. Felsztyn, for many years an engineering lecturer in Warsaw University, describes these tactics with especial reference to Oparin's book. (*Newman Association, Bulletin of the Philosophy of Science Group*, 1958, No 31). Every favourable comment in the West is quoted by the Russians with such comments as "even *bourgeois* Western scientists must accept the truth of the Soviet scientific teachings" while all criticisms are passed over in silence. Oparin's book was produced on purely Marxist lines as an attempt to prove the thesis of Engels about the origin of life. In Russia the true theory is (or used to be) distinguished from the false by whether it fits in with dialectical materialism.

[2] For example, G. A. Kerkut, *Implications of Evolution*, 1960.

rational way, but by merely mixing things at random and hoping that something alive will be produced! In the West such "experiments" are no longer taken seriously but in Russia they may receive great prominence. For example, in 1950 a Russian lady, Professor Olga Borisovna Lepeshinskaya, claimed to have made living matter out of parts of cells which are not usually considered to be concerned with genetics. Again, in 1963 a scientist at a Soviet Institute of Oceanography claimed to have made living organisms by placing copper and zinc plates in distilled water! After irresponsible claims of this kind have been made it appears that the aftermath is always the same: first there is wide publicity, later the claim is quietly dropped, by which time the public are diverted by another supposedly scientific disproof of religion.

Around the 1950's news reached Russia that in the West an increasing number of scientists had abandoned the old notion that man was descended from the apes. Authorities were disposed to place man's origin very far back in the past and to argue that apes, monkeys and men had a common ancestor. This view was violently opposed in Russia, for it was felt that it would greatly reduce the force of the argument for man's evolution. "It is not difficult," said Prezent, "to see that this sort of argument is utterly anti-Darwinian and patently leads to religious obfuscation."

Strange hoaxes were perpetrated in connexion with the perennial subject of resuscitation. In 1957 the Russians broadcast to the world that they had revived a giant whelk which had lain frozen in the ice for thousands of years. In 1963, again, Moscow Radio claimed that lizard-like animals which had been frozen for 5,000 years had been revived. Needless to say these reports were later repudiated, having turned out to be as baseless as the alleged discovery of extra-terrestrial life in a distant star in 1965.

Psychologically the Russians want to show that man has ultimate power over life, that life is not as complex as Western scientists suppose (and is therefore more likely to come into existence spontaneously) and that creatures as clever as men are to be found scattered all over the cosmos (thus falsifying the Christian view that man has received a unique revelation). The hope that man will be able to visit distant planets gives credence to stories of living creatures restored to life after thousands of years in cold storage.

The possibility that there is life elsewhere is easily linked with the idea that beings from other worlds have visited us, and this in turn can be used to discredit religion—for angels can be interpreted as pilots of flying saucers!

In 1960 a responsible journal, the *Moscow Literary Gazette*, published an article maintaining that space-ships from other planets have visited the earth on many occasions, some of them within historic times. The fire that Elijah called down from heaven, and the destruction of Troy, and of Sodom and Gomorrah, were said to have been caused by such visitations. In the last instance, surplus stock of nuclear fuel had been jettisoned and the inhabitants had been warned, but only Lot took the warning seriously. These views, which seem to have been taken very seriously in Russia (for they dispensed with the idea that God had been at work on earth in Bible times) were finally disowned by the Soviet Academy of Science. This body declared that, though possible, the theory ought not to be accepted as scientific because there was as yet no real evidence in its support. The plain fact would seem to be that the new theory proved too much. Atheistical Russian scientists have long pretended that science positively *proves* that all life on earth has evolved from lowly organisms and these again from non-living matter. But if there have been visitors from other planets, then new organisms must have been introduced on an unknown number of occasions and all the "evidence" that higher organisms have risen from lower ones becomes worthless. Close one loophole for theology and another, supposedly closed long ago, unexpectedly opens!

E. S. P.

Psychical research, too, is ambivalent. The accepted Russian doctrine has been—at least until very recently—that nature has a magic power of doing just what you want her to do; no need for elaborate mechanisms which might suggest to simple folk that they had been designed by God! Brains, ears, legs, eyes—all will come into existence for the asking if they are required by evolution. In 1963 a Russian girl turned up who, though blindfolded, could read print and distinguish colours through the tips of her fingers—forebodings, perhaps, of a new evolutionary stage to come! The story was uncritically accepted—though the girl was resorting to trickery.

As for telepathy,[1] this, like other forms of extra-sensory perception, was violently opposed until recently because it has been widely used in the West in support of religious ideas—and little research was conducted. But a few years ago the official attitude changed suddenly. It is said that the rumour got around that the U.S.A. Navy had learned how to communicate with deeply submerged submarines by telepathy! At once experiments were put in hand which, like those in the West, confirmed the reality of the phenomenon. A materialistic explanation (without evidence!) was confidently assumed and hope was entertained that it might make communication with astronauts possible. But hopes were soon dashed. No one has yet perfected telepathy to the point at which it is reliable enough to replace communication engineering!

For this long and sad story of the mistakes of Russian science it would seem that atheism is to blame: too often atheism encourages bad science; too often it leads its devotees to expect false results, while in his enthusiasm the atheist becomes uncritical.

WESTERN HOAXES

It is noteworthy too that even in the West, scientific hoaxes often appear to have had the same motivation as in Russia. The Piltdown forgery was motivated by a desire to spread Darwinism which in the popular mind of the Victorian Age was felt to be strongly anti-theological. It is old now, but the discovery that it was a forgery is modern. More recently Pekin man has been called in question and there is now strong evidence that it too is a hoax.[2] Again, the discovery of organisms on the Orgueil meteorite occasioned the publication of an enormous number of scientific studies—often sponsored by J. D. Bernal, a well-known atheist. But in this case one of the "species" was identified as local and it is

[1] See also p. 147.
[2] P. O'Connell, *Science Today and the Problems of Genesis,* St. Paul 1, Minnesota, U.S.A., 1959, pp. 108–38.

now thought that the meteorite (which fell in 1864) became contaminated before it was housed in the local museum.[1]

It would be instructive to compare this record with its opposite number—instances of cases in which religious people have allowed religion to distort or falsify their science.

In the nineteenth century this probably happened in geology and biology, chiefly in connexion with the evolutionary controversy. It is difficult, however, to find convincing modern examples. This is partly because Christians have learned to be less dogmatic and more careful, but partly also because the Christian outlook, applied to science, more often than not leads to the right results.

[1] The relative abundance of about twenty amino acids isolated from the Orgueil and similar carbonaceous meteorites follows a pattern closely similar to that of sweat from human fingers. See *Nature*, 1965, 207, 1043-5. It is worth noting in this connexion that Lord Kelvin, a convinced Christian, first suggested that just possibly God first made life in our solar system on another planet. This, he suggested, might later have been destroyed in a collision, producing meteorites which carried germs of life to the earth. (Presidential Address to the British Association, 1871.) The idea caused much discussion at the time, was immortalized by *Punch*, and figured again in letters to *The Times* towards the end of the century. Oddly enough it seems that not a single modern writer (up to 1966) has included Kelvin's name in this connexion—all early references to the possibility of life on meteorites being several decades later.

CHAPTER II

TESTIMONY—PSYCHOLOGY AND PARAPSYCHOLOGY

T HE CHRISTIAN FAITH IS FOUNDED UPON WHAT A sceptic must always regard as a tall story about a dead Man whom His followers claimed to be alive. These followers or disciples said that after their Leader had been killed by the authorities of the day He nevertheless appeared on several occasions and that finally, in the presence of more than 500 people, He rose into the air, disappeared in a cloud and after that was seen no more. In support of these astonishing stories many of the early disciples testified that they were eyewitnesses of these events.

TRUE?

Is this true? Or is it mythical? Or are we concerned with distortions of events which really happened, though not as recorded?

What kind of evidence will help us to decide? We cannot put dead men in the witness-box so we must resort to other methods. Firstly, we can examine the recorded testimony. Secondly, if the alleged witnesses started a movement, it ought to be possible to argue back historically concerning the movement, until we reach its origin. We might then be in a position to ask whether the alleged beginnings are consistent with the story which follows. A third method, often used in the past, might be to compare the events with phenomena which people can observe for themselves at the present time, in the hope that present-day knowledge would give us a yardstick of truth. In this form, of course, such a procedure can have no logical justification—for it might rightly be said that if the Christian story is unique it cannot be paralleled today: if it is not unique then parallel modern phenomena cannot support Christianity. Nevertheless, the inquiry might not prove valueless.

The Christian story can be tackled from all these angles. The first calls for a study of the value of evidence, and particularly of testimony, to which we shall return. The second affords evidence which, so far as it goes, strongly supports the view that very odd events must have occurred at the beginning of our era. We have to ask how, from a psychological angle, a group of despondent men, shattered by the death of their leader, became so confident that He was alive and triumphant, that they not only convinced themselves that this was so—just possible, perhaps—but started a movement which spread rapidly throughout the known world. We have to ask how a death, a sheer defeat by the standards of the world, came to be thought of as a triumph. It is difficult to answer these questions unless we assume that there was in fact a resurrection—at least of a kind. But we shall not pursue the matter here, as this has often been done before.

SCIENCE ENTERS THE PICTURE

What about the third line of attack? Can science provide us with a yardstick of probability with which to assess the evidence? And if the uniqueness, or alleged uniqueness, of Christianity makes this impossible, how can it help us? In science we do not like unique events. If we observe something odd we try, if we can, to reproduce the conditions again so to see if the phenomenon will recur. Obviously this is not possible with historical events. Science, then, has no *direct* bearing on the resurrection story. But indirectly, as we shall see, it can prove helpful.

A sceptic's attitude to the resurrection story might take either of two forms, according to whether he accepts or denies the fact that something highly unusual happened at the beginning of Christianity.

PSYCHOLOGY

Suppose he accepts this. It will then be a fairly safe bet that the Christian story will fall into line with other unexplained stories in which men have had collective hallucinations. In short, he will study its resemblances to hauntings, poltergeists, flying-saucer myths or other alleged queer happenings of today. He may reject the truth of all these beliefs, but nevertheless hold that the mere fact that man invents them brings them into the category of the psychology of man. Perhaps they are present as an archetype of some kind in the human psyche. But even if there is no easy explanation, he will expect the Christian story to hang together with the rest. In contrast, the Christian, just because he believes his religion to be unique, will not expect to find close parallels between the Christian resurrection and paranormal or odd events, real or imagined.

When we put the question in this form, we are faced at once with the fact that the differences between what we find in the Christian record and the inquiries which have been made by psychical researchers differ so greatly that it is hard to know just where to start the comparison.

Are there other cases of people having come out of their graves alive? Apparently not, though there have been cases of people presumed dead who were not really so. But these would seem to offer no comparison with Christianity. For Jesus did not return to the world of the living as an emaciated invalid recovering from terrible wounds: the disciples were not *sorry* for him. Instead He told them that all power was now in His hands and He was believed. They understood Him to be the conqueror of death: there was no question of His dying a second time.

. . . OR PARAPSYCHOLOGY

There are many cases of haunting recorded in which poltergeists throw stones, move the furniture, or make mysterious raps. Can we suggest that the garden tomb where Jesus was buried was haunted? Again, this makes little sense. The stone was moved and the body too, but that is about all by way of resemblance that we can find. There is no adolescent girl in the picture, no movement of a seemingly aimless or playful nature, no one to be terrified out of his wits!

Nor do the records of Christian origins fit in with the typical ghost story. Ghosts do not appear in broad daylight, still less talk for hours about serious topics with those who think they are normal in every way. (Jesus after His resurrection, was mistaken both as a gardener and as a stranger who had come to Jerusalem.) Ghosts, whatever their nature may be, seem to be associated with special localities—haunted houses, graveyards and so on. But Jesus appeared in a variety of places—in a garden, on the shore of a lake, on an ordinary road. Ghosts do not inspire people with their preaching. But Jesus spent a long time in conversation expounding the Scriptures so effectively that the disciples later said, "Did not our hearts burn within us ... ?" Again, it is difficult to find a point of comparison.

What about collective hallucinations created, say, by the expectation that Jesus would rise from the dead—some queer and little understood quirk of the human mind? But the difficulties are not less than before. Hallucinations are soon over and are not seen by all present. Suppose some of the people who were present on the occasions when Jesus was seen after his death—say, some of the five or six hundred who were present when He was finally seen to ascend into heaven—suppose *some* of them had seen nothing at all, is it conceivable that the Christian church would have come into existence? Those who saw nothing would have roundly declared that the others were lying. They would have testified that they had been there themselves on the occasions that were being talked about but had seen nothing unusual. Can we imagine that the early Christian church could have made headway if anything like this had happened?

Again, we can imagine that in some way an intense expectation may cause an image of what a man expects to form in his imagination. But theories of this kind become irrelevant when we reflect that the disciples did *not* expect anything strange to happen. After the death of Jesus, they lost hope. All were disillusioned. It was only as a result of the strange appearances that hope revived. It can hardly have been auto-suggestion, then, which brought about the appearances.

On the main issue, then, psychical research and psychology seem to throw no light whatever. The Christian is right in his expectation that the events which took place at the birth of Christianity will not fall into line with rare paranormal events which take place—or are alleged to take place—in all countries and times.

FALSE TESTIMONY?

The complete failure of this line of inquiry may lead the sceptic back to a still more sceptical position. The Christian stories are believed on the basis of human testimony. But is human testimony reliable? Can we trust people when they claim to have witnessed unusual events?

A natural reaction will be to say that there must have been a mistake somewhere, but it is now too late in the day to discover what really happened. After all, the whole story depends on the reliability of the testimony of the early disciples. But how reliable is testimony?

Here again we enter the field of science. For it is possible to design experiments to test the reliability of human testimony. Sometimes, also, we can check on the reliability of spontaneous testimony.

So once again, both the sceptic and the Christian are concerned with science at least in so far as it can tell us something about the value of testimony. The sceptic is obliged to believe that testimony is much less reliable than was formerly supposed. Only so can he excuse himself from becoming a Christian, for if the early Christians were right in what they claimed to have witnessed, Christianity follows as a matter of course. If, on the other hand, the human mind is so full of quirks that when men claim to have seen unusual things with their own eyes we can afford to ignore what they say unless there is abundant independent confirmation, then there may be good reasons why Christianity should not be believed. And if this is in fact true, then science is bound to bring it to light in the end. But if on the other hand the Christian is right in giving credence to the testimonies of early Christians, we should expect science to confirm the reliability of the testimony of the ordinary man in somewhat similar circumstances.

In the following two chapters we shall attempt to assess the trend of science in so far as it can lead to a decision between these two points of view.

CHAPTER 12

TESTIMONY—THE PROBLEM

TESTIMONY UNRELIABLE

HOW RELIABLE IS TESTIMONY CONCERNING UNUSUAL events? We have outlined the answers which the typical nineteenth-century Christian and sceptic respectively would have given to this question. It is clear that these answers are, in effect, prophecies of the results which would be obtained when science turned its attention to the study of the reliability of testimony. What, then, are the facts available today?

Until fairly recently the sceptic had a case. Firstly, he could point to disagreement in the stories of the resurrection appearances themselves. This seemed to support the unreliability of the testimony on which they rested. However, it is probably agreed by all today that this is not a very serious objection. If the stories had agreed exactly, critics would have said that they had been tampered with to make them agree. Certainly, they appear more spontaneous and convincing as they are. The differences are not greater than we may find today in accounts of the same incident which has been covered by reporters representing different papers, or of historical events which are not called in question.

A well-known historical example is afforded by the death of Mary Queen of Scots. When, around 1830–40 her body was exhumed, it was found that she had received not one, as had been thought, but *two* strokes from the executioner, the first only having slashed the nape of her neck. Of the many contemporary accounts, only one mentions more than one stroke and this gives the number of strokes as three: the others all state or imply that the executioner struck but once. Thus, in a minor point, the records of eyewitnesses have proved unreliable. Does this mean that those who cannot be relied upon to record trivial matters accurately, will be unrealiable too when serious matters are at stake? Most certainly it does not—and in this instance the main issue is unaffected, for no one doubts that the execution of Mary really did take place.[1] Similarly, if we assume (and it is far from proved) that discrepancies in the Gospels cannot be reconciled, we must not jump to the conclusion that the main Gospel story has been discredited. A more natural conclusion in all such cases would be that when peoples' minds are preoccupied with what to them is a supremely important matter, they may become less observant of relatively trivial detail.

Secondly, support for the sceptic came from the legal profession. At the end of the last century extreme scepticism began to be felt in some quarters about the value of evidence given under oath in courts of law. Increasingly it seemed that untrained people would often, without intending to deceive, make untrue or misleading statements under cross-examination. If this can happen in a civilized society, what reliance, it was asked, can we place upon testimonies which have come down to us from a backwater of the Roman Empire of two thousand years ago?

Before long the psychical researchers were at work; they too were interested parties and wished to know how far human testimony could be trusted when strange psychical happenings were reported. Professor Varendonck, for example, arranged for a man to enter a crowded lecture room, shout a few angry words and leave. Of the 325 accounts of the episode given by those present, it was estimated that only 116 were approximately correct. In later work conjurers attended séances in which the sitters knew that everything that happened would be done by normal means. Written accounts were examined and marks assigned for correct answers.

The "phenomena" were trivial. A door was opened and closed; a gramophone was stopped and a flash of light followed, sitters being asked to remember whether the flash took place in silence or otherwise; a tiny spot of light was made to appear over the "medium's" head; sitters were asked to detail the order of objects on a table from memory, and so on. The average score was only about a third of that possible.

[1] Hans Gross, *Criminal Investigation,* 5th ed. 1962, p. 48. See also, A. W. Stewart, *Alias J. J. Connington,* 1947, Chapter 7, "What is your Evidence Worth".

A long series of results of this kind,[1] conducted over many years, was interpreted to mean that an average human testimony was much less reliable than had been commonly supposed. Sceptics[2] enthusiastically quoted these results in justification for disbelief in the Christian miracles.

FEATURES OF CHRISTIAN TESTIMONY

These experiments, however, would seem to have little bearing on Christian testimony. The reliability of testimony is not to be confused with the ability to remember and describe happenings of trivial importance. It is a matter of common knowledge that as a man looks back on his life, episodes which have influenced him radically stand out vividly in his memory—the "turning points of our destiny" are "burnt into our memories"[3]—while "experiences which are accompanied by strong emotions are remembered longer and are more vividly recalled than those accompanied by weak emotions".[4] The question we must ask is not whether a man's testimony is trustworthy when he swears that it was a blue car and not a green one that passed him on the road, or whether a man slammed a door after or before shouting a slogan, but whether events which profoundly influence our lives are correctly remembered.

The second feature of the early Christian testimony is the extremely unusual nature of the events which are described. Here again, unusual sights fix themselves on the memory. On returning home, we might not notice consciously whether smoke was rising from the chimney, but we should notice immediately if the smoke was coming from a window. Unusual events tend, of course, to link up with changes in our fortune—a fire might well cause a profound change in one's manner of living.

Testimony concerning the unusual often involves a man in the risk of becoming a social outcast if he proves to be wrong. The

[1] From those of Hodgson and Davey (*Soc. Psy. Res. Proceedings*, 1886, **4**, 381) to that of Bestermann (ibid. 1932, **40**, 363).
[2] For example, I. A. Tucker, *The Evidence for the Supernatural*, 1911; C. D. Broad, *Philosophy*, 1939, **14**, 131.
[3] John Martin–Harvey (Sir), *Autobiography*, 1933, p. 36.
[4] W. B. Pillsbury, *Attention*, 1908, p. 103.

man who calls a fire brigade when his house is *not* on fire will find that his mistake is long remembered against him. It is the risk of being placed outside the social group, in extreme cases of suffering persecution or worse, which encourages men to use their critical faculties to the full extent when they testify to anything highly unusual. This ensures that a man will make as certain of his facts as he possibly can before he commits himself. And this is the situation we find in Christianity. The early disciples were so certain of what they had seen and heard that they risked not only ridicule but bitter persecution and often death.

These considerations call into question the doubts which have been cast on the reliability of early Christian testimony in recent years. To evaluate this testimony we must adopt a different procedure.

SEARCH FOR ANALOGY

For comparison, what we need is to find cases of people who have testified to witnessing exceedingly unusual events and who have stuck to their stories in the face of criticism and disbelief. It is here that science can help us, for very rare natural events, quite inexplicable in terms of the science of the day, have sometimes occurred. Can we find relevant records which have come down to us from the past? If so, then on applying the yardstick of more recent science, shall we recognize the descriptions as substantially correct? Or shall we find the testimony of human beings in the pre-scientific era to be so hopelessly confused and imaginative that it makes little or no scientific sense today?

But why, it may be asked, must we delve into the past? Are there not many people today who testify that they have seen strange things?

The difficulty is that these recent examples do not provide a parallel to the testimony of the Christian disciples. We need to take our examples from the days before all such evidence was made suspect by the methods of modern mass propaganda. Today, regrettably, if you can find no other way of making a sensation you can do so be telling a yarn—about your chat with friendly denizens of Mars who obligingly got out of their flying saucer on a lonely road, or how when you saw Christ appear in a tree you were smart enough to take a snap (photograph for sale, of course), or how you fared in your harrowing encounter with the monster which emerged from a renowned lake, or how you travelled to the Levant (you had never left the country, of course) and were entertained by a black prince (doubtless the Antichrist) who worked miracles in your presence and told you that he was soon going to rule the world. . . . Today a man has but to stick to his story and it will bring him not suffering but television interviews, lecture tours, serial rights, perhaps a best-seller, renown and wealth.

At times the same happened in the past. Without a doubt the "sentinel" of the jail (and his assistant who corroborated his story) where a witch was confined knew on which side his bread was buttered when "he avowed that he saw a scroll of paper creep from under the prison door, and then change itself first into a monkey and then into a turkey".[1] But except when some popular mania was abroad, it can hardly have been profitable to "witness" such strange goings-on—there was often risk of incarceration in a lunatic asylum! At all events we are safer with the past than the present. What we need is to go back in time to days when a man usually had to live with his testimony without hope of reward.

Once again, the result of such an inquiry has a direct bearing on the divergence of opinion between the sceptic and the Christian. The sceptic who may wish to render plausible the view that the testimony offered in the Bible is false or mistaken, might well expect all human testimony in the circumstances we have described to be relatively worthless. On the other hand, the Christian, who accepts the general reliability of testimony, would expect such testimony to be on the whole reliable—not necessarily in every detail but at least in broad outline.

We may start by asking, what *kind* of evidence should we examine? The features we must look for are evidently these. The phenomena must be rare; they must be of a kind which might ordinarily provoke scepticism, and we must be able to find descriptions at least reasonably detailed. (With the exception of historical events, recorded by chroniclers, court recorders and "VIP's" in private correspondence, *highly* detailed descriptions

[1] Sir Walter Scott, *Letters on Demonology and Witchcraft*, 1830 (1884 ed., p. 218).

coming from earlier times—before the days of cheap paper and typewriters—are always hard to come by.)

Cases which we must definitely exclude are those in which a man is made a centre of attraction—as when a drunk tells a good story to his inebriated friends in a tavern about the devil he saw in a dark lane—or stories extracted by psychological pressure or even physical torture as was usual in the witchcraft trials. Owing to the lack of records or the difficulty in finding them if they exist, it may often be difficult to prove that the scepticism was contemporaneous with the testimony and so we may have to be content with accounts which seem odd enough to provoke disbelief and which we know were later disbelieved.

STONES FROM HEAVEN

Records fulfilling these conditions may be found. For example, it was an ancient belief that stones sometimes fall from heaven. Aristotle explained this by saying that mineral veins, when they are exposed at the surface of a rock, slowly evaporate and rise into the air where, after they have condensed to form meteorites, they later fall down to earth, usually in storms. In the seventeenth century however, it became clear that minerals do not evaporate in this way, so that the "explanation" was evidently wrong. There was no other explanation to take its place: in addition, it seemed most unscientific to imagine that stones could be loitering aloft ready to fall at any time upon the unwary—did not the law of gravity demand that if they had once been there they would have fallen long ages ago?

An easy way out of the difficulty was to deny that stones ever fall from the sky, and this view was at one time held by nearly all educated men. Stories of meteorites were relegated to old wives' tales. Shamefaced custodians of museums discarded their collections of alleged meteorites: Copernicus, Galileo, Kepler, Newton, Huygens and in later days Lavoisier joined in the general disbelief and it was noted disdainfully that the stones from heaven never fell when scientifically trained men were present.

Despite this doctrinaire attitude on the part of the learned world, however, meteorites continued to fall as before and the falls were sometimes witnessed. But it made no difference: the scientists stood their ground. When Lavoisier was shown a meteorite which had recently fallen he said that lightning must have struck an ordinary piece of rock and broken a piece off. On one occasion a whole village, backed by the mayor, sent a signed statement to the Paris Academy to say that they had witnessed a fall. The Academy professed itself deeply shocked at their credulity and again pronounced that the event was physically impossible. The story is told that at about the same time President Thomas Jefferson of the U.S.A. heard of the report of two Yale Professors concerning the fall of meteorites near Weston, Connecticut in 1807 and said, "I should rather believe that those two Yankee Professors would lie than believe that stones fall from heaven."[1]

This attitude on the part of the educated world did not change till the beginning of the nineteenth century and then, only, because there happened to be a shower uncomfortably near to Paris itself! Today, of course, there is no question about the genuineness of the phenomenon but, as Paneth remarks, accurate accounts of the falls of these bodies have come down to us from all ages.

Here then is a case of the type we need. But if we collect anecdotal instances of this kind it will be difficult to do so impartially. Some might favour Christian expectations; others those of non-Christians. In the latter category might be placed the remarkably detailed story of how John Frederick Helvetius turned lead into gold on a certain day in January 1667 at the Hague, using an elixir which had been left him by a stranger who claimed to be an alchemist. Helvetius had previously been sceptical as to the possibility of alchemy; he had even written against it, but was converted by the result of his own experience. Impossible in the light of today![2]

[1] Clyde Fisher, *The Story of the Moon*, 1945, p. 159. For stories of the incredulity which meteorites occasioned, see the standard works: F. A. Paneth, *The Origin of Meteorites*, 1940; F. Heide, *Meteorites* (Eng. Trans.) Chicago, 1964; E. L. Krinov, *Principles of Meteorites*, (Eng. Trans.) 1960.

[2] Helvetius did not suffer for his new opinion: rather, he became a hero in his limited circle, for in his day alchemy was widely accepted as possible. For a translation of Helvetius's book (1667) describing the transmutation see A. E. Waite, *The Secret Tradition in Alchemy*, 1926, Chapter 20.

Some stories tell one way: some the other. How shall we know which to choose? It would be desirable to consider all the records in, say, the British Museum Library and to treat them statistically. But this would require an army of workers.

In the next chapter we shall examine a possible approach.

CHAPTER 13

TEST CASE—PHOSPHORESCENT
APPEARANCES

COLD LIGHT

SOME YEARS BACK THE WRITER WAS ENGAGED FOR A considerable time in searching for early stories of luminous phenomena, with no thought whatever of their possible bearing on the value of testimony. Indeed, the possibility of using the material for this purpose did not dawn upon him until about three-quarters of the work had been completed. It is necessary to point this out lest it should be thought that the literature had been hastily scanned in order to prove a particular point of view, and thus much material of an opposing character had been omitted.

It eventually became clear that luminescent phenomena afford a favourable parallel to miracle. The literature abounds with records of the stark terror which luminous appearances have occasioned in the minds of simple people. Luminous pieces of meat have repeatedly been mistaken for ghosts, St. Elmo's fire was once considered a divine prodigy, while will-o'-the-wisps were once thought to be connected with wandering souls, and so on. Thus, like religion, luminous appearances have been connected with prejudice and emotion from time immemorial, and it is commonly supposed that under these circumstances human testimony is especially likely to be untrustworthy. Thus testimony in connexion with unusual luminous appearances should afford a parallel with the testimony on which the Christian faith rests.

A list of cases in which persons are alleged to have witnessed some definite and unusual phenomenon connected with luminous appearances, in which also testimonies were doubted by contemporaries or turned aside as ridiculous and "unscientific" by a subsequent generation, was compiled.[1] They were classified into three groups as follows: (*a*) cases in which subsequent

[1] R. E. D. Clark, *Jour. of Trans. of Victoria Institute*, 1940, **72**, 156, where further references to sources will be found.

investigation makes it highly probable that the original testimonies are substantially correct; (*b*) cases in which modern knowledge has thrown no new light upon the problem; and (*c*) cases in which it now appears that the original statements were so far from the truth that scepticism was justified.

As the object is to test *religious* testimony by independent testimony of a non-religious type, it seems best to omit cases of unexplained lights in connexion with religious beliefs and practices. In addition claims made by psychically "gifted" people are not included, since such people do not even claim to see events as an ordinary person might see them.

METEORITES. Meteorites are relevant here because, when a shower of stony meteorites falls, there is often not only a terrifying sound and the formation of thick cloud, but the sky may later become brightly luminescent and may stay so for a considerable time. A familiar record of this kind, often made a butt for ridicule by sceptics, is the Biblical story of how a shower of large stones, falling in the evening, was followed by a night which remained light enough for Joshua to complete the rout of the enemy (*Joshua* 10: 11)[1] The sun, or heavenly light behind the clouds, "stayed in the midst of heaven, and hasted not to go down about a whole day".[2] After the Siberian meteorite of 1908 newspapers could be read at midnight in England, and an illuminated sky at night has been associated with many lesser falls.

ELECTRICAL DISCHARGES. There are many records of light due to

[1] It is fascinating to note that at the time when scientists were sceptical of meteorites, this passage together with *Psalm* 18: 13, made Edward King, F.R.S., sceptical of their scepticism! For many years he collected records and was convinced that science would vindicate their truth. His book, *Remarks concerning Stones said to have fallen from the Clouds* . . . was published in 1796, just after but independently of Chladni's work (Chladni was the first scientist, in the modern era, to convince the learned world of the reality of meteorites). King was a staunch Christian and a man of great learning.

[2] It seems unlikely (at least to the author!) that the passage was intended to teach that the earth stopped rotating. The language is obviously poetic and is partly printed as poetry in R.V. and R.S.V., so it must not be taken too literally. The sun was not literally "at Gibeon", or the moon literally "in" a valley (see R.S.V.). Only in poetic language can we speak of the sun as a conscious being which can "hasten" to go down at night, etc.

electrical discharges. Pliny mentions stars which appear over land and sea. "I have seen," he writes, "a light in that form on the spears of soldiers." He also describes them on the rigging of ships, and remarks that such lights "do sometimes, about the evening, rest on mens' heads and are a great and good omen. But these are among the awful mysteries of nature". Virgil describes such a star on the head of Iulius, and from the context it is clear that the weather was stormy. Again, there are many records of the mysterious ball lightning, but until not very long ago it was fashionable to deny their truth on the ground that the phenomenon was inexplicable. Today, tongues of flame and globular lightning are well established.

Despite their religious bearing, the stories of phosphorescence connected with Moses are worth mentioning here. The account of the burning bush (*Exodus* 3: 2) was long deemed incredible by sceptics, as was also the story that on one occasion the face of Moses was luminous without his being aware of the fact. However, R. L. Ives[1] describes similar phenomena at high altitudes on the American Rockies. "Coronas, halos, and standing arcs have several times been observed by the writer when spending the night at very high altitudes (above 12,000 feet). These phenomena, never twice the same, sometimes attain considerable brilliance . . . often when coronas are present a person will, apparently, be bathed in flames although he himself will be unaware of it. . . . . At times the source of a corona will give very severe electric shocks when touched; at other times it seems electrically 'dead' and may be contacted with impunity."

Many stories have been told of luminous "twisters" and these are sometimes so bizarre "that there is reason to believe that some tornado observations may have been subject to a kind of scientific censorship". On 11 April 1965 at Toledo, near Lake Erie, twisters passed through the town at night and were, almost accidentally, photographed when they were clearly seen as great columns of light. A critical study of earlier literature, which had largely been discounted before, now makes it clear that earlier stories are substantially reliable.[2]

[1] R. L. Ives, *Jour. Franklin Instit.*, 1938, pp. 226, 745.
[2] B. Vonnegut and J. R. Weyer, *Science*, 1966, **153**, 1213.

EARTHQUAKE LIGHTS. From earliest times (e.g. Tacitus on the earthquake which destroyed the Achaian cities in 373 B.C.), legend associates earthquakes with brilliant lights. In the quake at Mutu, in North Japan, in A.D. 869, "streaming light was seen as if it was daytime": in the Kramakura earthquake of A.D. 1257, bluish flames came from the ground and a fireball like a lantern flew across the sky, while in the Tosa earthquake of A.D. 1283, fire-balls appeared in the shape of wheels and flew in all directions. Scores of similar statements are to be found in the old records and though these are scattered over many centuries they are said to show considerable uniformity.[1] Nevertheless, until around 1930 seismologists ascribed the records to the imagination of simple people who might easily be expected to fancy they saw vivid lights if their houses were falling around them.

Since 1930 this explanation has been generally abandoned. After the Idu earthquake of 26 November 1930, Mr. Musya of the Japanese Earthquake Research Institute circulated all schools within the affected area asking for independent accounts of any lights which had been seen; 1,500 reports were received, which included those from no less than fifteen trained scientists. The light appeared in the sky before the earthquake and just above the epicentre. It was computed that it must have had an intensity of at least 100,000,000 candle-power. There is still no generally accepted explanation.

THE AURORA POLARIS. The aurora affords another case in which human testimony has been strongly opposed by science. Long ago scientists showed that the streamers were rarely less than a hundred miles from an observer. Despite this, many people confidently asserted that the streamers often come right down to earth, and that their movements were associated with sound. Such statements were made by reliable witnesses—one or two of which had actually received training in surveying.[2] Yet the scientific grounds for supposing that such phenomena were impossible

---

[1] These records were collected by K. Musya and T. Terada, see *Earthquake Research Bull*, 1931, **9**, 177, 225.

[2] C. S. Beals, *Quart. Jour. Roy. Met. Soc.*, 1933, **59**, 71. 7. References to earlier literature are given in W. H. Stewart's, *A New System of Nature*, 2 vols., Glasgow, 1861, p. 196.

seemed so strong, that until comparatively recently they were often ascribed to optical and auditory illusions. It seems likely, however, that illuminated columns of mist arising from lakes may sometimes appear to join the steamers above. The noises were at first explained as due to changes in the electrical condition of the air, but when instruments failed to detect the supposed changes, the noises were attributed to imagination. One writer thought he had finally disposed of the matter by asserting (on medical authority!) that 50 per cent of people suffer from noises in the head.

In 1938 Carl Störmer,[1] at that time the worlds greatest authority on the aurora, was himself reluctantly convinced of the reality of the sounds as a result of the auroral displays in that year. Several of his assistants stationed at different observatories heard the sound rising and falling as the streamers passed overhead. It seems that as yet no explanation is adequate.

THE LANDFALL OF COLUMBUS. At about ten o'clock on the night of 11 October 1492, about four hours before he made his landfall, Columbus claimed to have seen what looked like the flame of a small candle which appeared to rise and fall on the surface of the water. The light has occasioned much controversy, as it must have been in deep water some thirty-five miles out to sea—too far out for native boats to venture at night. J. B. Murdock, of the U.S. Navy, after a careful review of the subject, concluded that the light was due to the overwrought fancies of the navigators.[2] L. R. Crawshay, however, pointed out that the light might well have been caused by a surface display of the luminous marine annelids of the genus *odontosyllis*.[3] The displays occur once a month only, for a few moments, in the last quarter of the moon.

FLASHES OF LIGHT FROM PLANTS. Josephus mentions a certain plant with a yellow flower ("Its colour is like that of flame") which "towards the evening sends out a ray like lightning". In modern times this identical phenomenon was first observed, it is believed,

[1] *Nature*, 1938, **141**, 232, 946.
[2] See R. T. Gould, *Geographical Mag.*, 1927, **69**, 403.
[3] *Nature*, 1935, **136**, 559.

by the daughter of Linnaeus in 1762, while she was still a girl. She declared that a group of yellow nasturtiums had flashed with a "lightning-like phosphorescence" in the evening twilight. For many years she was laughed at and even accused of lying, but she stuck to her story. Subsequent research by Professor Haggern and others showed that many flowers, especially yellow ones, possess the power of emitting flashes of light at dusk.[1]

LUMINOUS BIRDS. In ancient times Pliny wrote: "In the Hercynian Forest, in Germany, we hear of a singular kind of bird, the feathers of which shine at night like fire." In the seventeenth century luminous birds were repeatedly observed; Bartholin, for example, mentions several luminous cocks brought to market at Montpellier in 1641.[2] Yet in later years the great natural historian, Cuvier, unable to see any reason why birds should be luminous, boldly declared that Pliny's statement was a mere poetical exaggeration. In modern times Mr. R. J. W. Purdy found to his cost that an account of luminous owls which he had published was merely laughed at by his fellow naturalists, who had not seen such things for themselves. Yet the existence of such owls in now generally conceded, while the night heron and the blue crane have also been seen in a luminous condition.[3]

GLOW-WORMS AND FIRE-FLIES. A relatively enormous literature has collected round the glow-worm. Early experimenters claimed to be able to extract a luminous juice from the insect, but scientists believed that the light was in some way connected with life, and so refused to believe in the luminous liquid. "Some have told me that this is very true," writes the learned Moffett,[4]

---

[1] T. L. Phipson, *Phosphorescence or the Emission of Light by Minerals, Plants and Animals,* 1862, p. 79. The author is not aware of modern literature on this subject.

[2] *De luce animalium,* 1647. Bartolin wondered whether, if a luminescent cock fell in love with a luminescent hen, a race of incandescent fowls might be produced!

[3] R. J. W. Purdy, *The Field,* 1908, **3**, 70; *Trans. Norfolk and Norwich Naturalists' Society,* 1908, **8**, 547; Count L. de Sibour, *Knowledge,* 1913, **36** 321; H. W. Robinson, *The Field,* 1930, **155**, 230.

[4] Thomas Moffett (variously spelt Moffit, Moufet), *History of Fourfooted Beasts and Serpents,* 1658, p. 979.

"whom not-withstanding, I will not believe until such time as the experiment be made before my eyes." Sir Thomas Browne also considered the matter in his *Pseudodoxia Epidemica* and roundly declared that the feat was impossible. Yet we know today that the extraction of the luminous material from the organs of an insect is not a difficult matter and seeing that repeated efforts were made to achieve it, there is no need to doubt that they were sometimes crowned with success a few centuries ago. Extracts from fireflies are now prepared by space technologists who use them as a test for living organisms in the high atmosphere. "ATP", present in all living matter, causes the extract to emit light.

The synchronous flashing of fireflies has occasioned much interest in the present century. Here again, scientists such as Craig (1916) and Ruckmick (1920) denounced the phenomenon as imaginary simply because they could not explain it. Ruckmick went so far as to declare that the observations were always made in an emotional state of mind "bordering on the romantic", and so were necessarily untrustworthy. Today no biologist doubts that the phenomenon is genuine; it has even proved possible to reproduce it under controlled conditions in the laboratory, though the ability of the insects to control their flashing to an accuracy of around one hundredth of a second is ill-understood.[1]

WILL-O'-THE-WISPS. Will-o'-the-wisps have had a long and interesting history about which something may now be said. One variety is apparently caused by the spontaneous ignition of bubbles of marsh gas—though the cause of the ignition is not known. The circumstantial and matter-of-fact accounts of eyewitnesses leave little to be desired. Nevertheless, the fact that no explanation was forthcoming, caused many German scientists in the nineteenth century to ridicule the phenomenon—though Knorr, a well-known physicist, described in detail how he had himself seen one at close quarters. Today little further information is available, but it is known that volatile compounds of metallic elements may be formed as a result of the action of autotrophic bacteria, and as some of these are spontaneously inflammable, it seems only

[1] See J. B. and E. Buck, *Nature*, 1966, **211**, 562–4, where earlier references are given.

reasonable to take the stories at their face value.[1] Since the draining
of the land in the nineteenth century the phenomenon has become
much rarer, but it is interesting to note that lights appearing
suddenly in *marshy* land are now, not infrequently, attributed to
flying saucers![2]

LUMINOUS HUMAN BEINGS AND "SPONTANEOUS COMBUSTION".
There are numerous eyewitness accounts of luminous human
beings. Lord Bacon solemnly declared that he had seen a "woman's
belly sparkling with fire", while numerous doctors in later years
witnessed and published accounts of the same phenomenon.
Despite this wealth of human testimony, experiment seemed to
show that luminous bacteria would not live on human skin, and in
1905 the *British Medical Journal* quoted the words of Bacon to
illustrate the supposed credulity of former generations![3]

An interesting modern case, published by F. Barton, a detective,
led to the conviction of a murderer in Singapore at the end of the
First World War, but no scientific investigation was made.[4] A
better-known case is that of Mrs. Anna Monaro, an ascetic Italian
woman, which took place in a hospital in the fishing town of
Pirano, on the Istrian coast, in 1934.[5] This received full scientific
publicity, and, in Italy, a book on the case was published. This
lady's chest became brightly luminous for three to four seconds at
a time—the flashes being repeated for up to twenty-five times in a
night. The light was successfully recorded on cinematograph film.
After this case, witnessed by many scientists and doctors, scepticism virtually ceased.[6]

[1] For references see also R. E. D. Clark, *Will-o'-the-wisp*, School Science
Review, February 1942, p. 138.

[2] An article in *Time and Tide*, (6 April 1966, p. 11) described saucers in the
Ann Arbor area, Mich. U.S.A. "An object that pulsated, landed in a swamp,"
it "moved up and down and sideways". "Odd thing—all reports—they come
down in swampy areas." See also *Life*, 18 April 1966.

[3] *British Med. Jour.*, 1905, *ii*, 346. See also R. E. D. Clark, *Biological Light*,
School Science Review, 1936, p. 249. Sequeira, Ingram and Brain, in *Diseases
of the Skin*, 5th ed. 1947, p. 726 takes the subject seriously and attributed the
phosphorescence to bacteria.

[4] *Wide World Magazine*, 1934, **73**, 61.

[5] See Medical Press for April and May.

[6] G. Protti, *Riforma Medica*, 1934, *i*, 841. Summaries appeared in many
English journals, e.g. *Lancet*, 1934, **227**, 1403.

The story of the "spontaneous combustion" of human beings is rather similar. Here again, there was excellent testimony to hand—not indeed for the actual combustion of a *living* person but for the fact that bodies had sometimes been found burnt or burning in rooms where people had been alone. Dickens, in *Bleak House*, said that there would have to be a spontaneous combustion of human testimony itself before all the stories could be dismissed. Nevertheless, it was customary to pour ridicule on the idea. However, it is now known that in some cases, after death, there is an enormous generation of inflamable gas in the bodies of alcoholics. This, when ignited, burns with a pale lambent flame—such flames are reported in older records—and there seems no doubt that on occasions when such a man died by the fireside and the gas later took fire, it would have been reported as a case of spontaneous combustion. Today there is no need to doubt this horrible phenomenon, which may well have been relatively common in the intemperate nineteenth century.[1]

Occasionally, in cases of pyloric stenosis an inflammable gas (analyses give 20–30 per cent hydrogen, up to 10 per cent methane, hydrogen sulphide and CO_2) collects in the stomach and on eructation reaches the mouth. Over a dozen cases are recorded in the standard medical journals over the past century (the last, *Lancet*, 1944, **247**, 114) in which, on lighting a match or attempting to smoke, an explosion has followed, or blue flames have appeared at nose or mouth. The bang sent one unfortunate man's cigarette flying across several rows of seats in a cinema (*Lancet*, 1934, **227**, 252)!

CONCLUSION

These are the only phenomena encountered which have a reasonable ground for inclusion in the list. Not a single good case was found in which we, today, would feel confident that the original testimony was wrong. Occasionally, of course, as with the aurora streamers coming down to earth, witnesses merely described what they saw but apparently misinterpreted. Sometimes, there is

[1] See Mann's *Forensic Medicine and Toxicology*, (6th ed. 1922, p. 215) for a case admitted to Guy's Hostpital, London, in the present century. Also discussion in D. Kerr, *Forensic Medicine*, 1936, p. 110.

exaggeration—particularly in odd remarks made by ancient writers who gave no detail. But it is hard to find a single clear instance of a palpably false story.

It is reasonable to conclude that science today underlines the reliability of human testimony. This conclusion has also been reached by others. For example, as far back as 1893, in a paper given to the Psychical Congress at Chicago, Alfred Russell Wallace (who shared the credit for the evolutionary theory with Charles Darwin) said, "The whole history of science shows that whenever the educated and scientific men of the age have denied the facts of other investigators on *a priori* grounds of absurdity or impossibility, the deniers have always been wrong."[1] Even if we hold that this statement is a little exaggerated, it cannot be far from the truth. It can no longer be seriously doubted that, on the whole, the facts concerning human testimony are in accordance with Christian rather than with atheist expectations.

OBSERVERS

A final point concerns observers themselves. The taunt that Christian evidences come only from untrained observers of a prescientific age is paralleled by the similar taunt that meteorites never fell in the presence of scientists. This raises the question whether the scientist, or the trained observer, is better able to observe what lies outside his own field than any other person.

Probably he is not. Science trains us to look for effects which we might anticipate if our theories are true; not to look for what is totally unexpected and unpredictable. Many stories are told of trained scientists who have been so conditioned by their theories that they have failed to observe what an untrained person would almost certainly have seen.

Sceptics often complain that the standard of evidence provided by the New Testament is not high enough because the early Christians, however sincere, were untrained as observers. Apart from the anachronism involved, it is hard to see the force of the argument. It is the very fact that ordinary people were involved

[1] Quoted, R. H. Newton, *The Arena*, 1890, May.

which makes their testimony so telling. Trained observers would probably have distrusted their senses, or allowed their views as to what they thought probable or improbable to colour their observations. We may be thankful indeed that the early disciples were not graduates of an ancient academy.

CHAPTER 14

SCIENCE AND HISTORY

SACRED HISTORY

THE BIBLE, AT LEAST IN PART, IS A HISTORY BOOK. BUT it differs a good deal from the history books we have today. On either side of the small territory occupied by Israel and Judah were large and powerful kingdoms engaged, seemingly endlessly, in spasmodic border skirmishes. Inevitably the fortunes of Israel depended upon those of her powerful neighbours. Sandwiched between the giants, should she align herself with Egypt or her northern neighbour? What form should alliances take? Could she play in both camps? What were the risks that the treasures stored in Jerusalem might tempt an army on the move to march inland from the coastal route?

Problems such as these, we might suppose, would fill a history book of Israel. But not so. The historians of this little country do not write as if their great neighbours were very important: it was their own country which mattered. As we read we gain the impression that here and here only some cosmic drama was being enacted, a drama never to be repeated, which would one day concern the whole world. The politics of the day seem of little importance: in the last resort only one thing matters—how far is the nation faithful to its religious heritage?

It is small wonder that a modern generation revolted against this indigenous and spiritual interpretation of history. In the modern era many atheists, in particular, have predicted confidently that a science of history would develop which, by explaining historical events without recourse to God, would make God an unnecessary hypothesis and expose the fallacy that underlies the Biblical story. But Christians, we may safely say, expected nothing of the kind as the final outcome of historical research.

THE LAW OF HISTORY

Science depends upon two things—there must be a repetition of events, and there must be a system of laws to account for the repetition. To what extent may we find these two factors in the history of mankind?

In the years before the Second World War many historians devoted their energies to the creation of scientific history. For Ostwald Spengler,[1] history was concerned with the rise and fall of civilizations. The story of each was essentially the same. Even the great leaders of one civilization had their near counterparts in all the others. In each of them religion declined with the rise of science. In their broad outline events are not unique.

Numerous attempts were made to discover the law or laws at the back of history. Discarding older pre-scientific theories, such as astrology, or the periodic reincarnations of prophets, many new theories were proposed. The laws might be economic, or the course of history might be determined by wars, or by diseases which from time to time decimated mankind, or by the erosion of the soil which spells inevitable doom to each great empire in turn, or by the rise and fall of ambitious young men bent on conquest, or by the decay of morals which sets in when a certain standard of comfort has been attained, or by sunspots which determine trade cycles,[2] or by a little understood civilizing factor which moves, travelling westward, in the form of rhythmic waves with a period of 850 years,[3] or by an inexorable evolutionary law which drives mankind onward towards the classless society (Karl Marx), or by the laws of psychoanalysis which apply to societies as well as to individuals, or by sinister plots devised by world-wide Jewry (the Nazi theory), or . . . . When once you have found the peg on which to hang the tangled story of mankind, all that is needed is for the details to be put in their places. This done, history "is a science, no less and no more"—no longer must it be thought of as an art where truth and accuracy are not of overriding importance.[4]

[1] *Decline of the West, 1926–8.*
[2] H. S. Jevons, *The Sun's Heat and Trade Activity*, 1910.
[3] See A. B. Gough, *Sociological Review*, 1936, **28**, 361.
[4] H. B. Bury, who was Professor of History at Cambridge from 1903.

ALL OR NOTHING TECHNIQUE

Some of these views seem quixotic in the extreme. It seems odd that otherwise sensible people should once have thought that a complex subject like history could be reduced to law and order in so simple a fashion. But this kind of thinking was not peculiar to historians, nor did it originate with them. Physical science had already achieved amazing success by the all-or-nothing technique. When once the cause of a phenomenon had been discovered, early scientists saw no need to look elsewhere for another cause. This attitude spread far beyond physical science. We encounter it, for example, in medicine, including psychological medicine. At one time a vast amount of all-or-nothing research was carried out on insanity in the belief that all the psychologist had to do was to discover its one and only physical cause. "Within my own memory," says Professor Strecker, "there was a time when it was thought that mental illnesses were caused by certain areas of focal infection—teeth, tonsils or whatnot—which if removed, so it was assumed, would cause all mental difficulties to disappear."[1] (At one time even crime was supposed to be caused by an infection!) One professor of psychology, who disapproved of the focal infection theory, remarked that his colleagues were frantically engaged in reducing colons to semi-colons—though to no good purpose! It took a long time for the medical psychologists to learn that progress was not to be won so easily.

In physical medicine the same attitude was prevalent until fairly recently. Innumerable teeth, glands, etc., were removed in the hope of effecting magic cures of headache, backache, rheumatism and other complaints.

In history, as in other fields, the temptation to apply the methods of physical science proved well-nigh irresistible. The historian began to feel that he had but to find the true cause which made the wheels of history turn and he would have joined the immortals with Newton. He would have become the creator of scientific history. Though a thousand failed in this alluring quest, someone would succeed in the end. Faith in the possibility of scientific history grew and prospered. And the more it grew, so the more did it seem that one more nail had been hammered in the

[1] E. A. Strecker, *Psychiatric Research*, 1947, p. 107,

coffin of Christianity. For Bible history is, as we have noted, a once-for-all affair; something unique, never to be repeated. But if history moves in great circles, with events repeating, the Bible is wrong. And if modern research proves that the true key to history is not the relation of a nation to its God but something else, then there is no need to trouble further with outworn ideas. These old notions must be allowed to pass away into the mists of history along with astrology, phlogiston and other mistakes of the past.

DEATH OF SCIENTIFIC HISTORY

In recent decades it has become clear to most historians that this approach must be abandoned. Indeed, scientific history seems now to be a thing of the past—at least in the western world. It was attacked vigorously and effectively by G. M. Trevelyan, while H. A. L. Fisher has said, "Men wiser and more learned than I have discerned in history a plot, a rhythm, a predetermined pattern. These harmonies are concealed from me. I can only see one emergency following upon another as wave follows upon wave. There can be no generalization, but only one safe rule for the historian: that he should recognize in the development of human destinies the play of the unforeseen and the contingent."[1]

The unforeseen! The shape of Cleopatra's nose; a parahelion appearing in the sky and interpreted by the Emperor Constantine as a symbol of the conquering Christ; an ambiguity in the utterance of the Delphic oracle; the omission in error of a prohibition of missiles in the Versailles Treaty after the First World War; a dream of Hitler to the effect that not one of his secret rocket weapons would land on English soil;[2] a single act of kindness shown to a young person which saves him from bitterness—these are the materials which, so often, history feeds into her loom. Unpredictable, unrepeatable, seemingly fortuitous and trivial—they cannot form the foundations of exact science. What science could there be if the accuracy of an astronomer's clock depended on whether a

[1] H. A. L. Fisher, *History of Europe*, 1936, Preface.

[2] W. Dornberger, *V*2, (Eng. Trans.) 1954. In March 1943 strenuous attempts were made to pursuade Hitler to agree to the large-scale production of rockets. The decisive message came through: "The Führer has dreamed that no A4 will ever reach England," p. 92.

caterpillar a mile off was chewing cabbage or lettuce; or the reliability of a chemical analysis on the chemist's horoscope?

HISTORY AND SCIENCE

Christians were right: history *is* unique. But what shall we say about the way the Bible interprets history? To answer this, let us compare the interpretations of the historian with those of the scientist.

Why are science and history so different? The reason is that in science we can simplify our problems. We can measure the current flowing through a wire or the volume of gas evolved in a chemical reaction confident that the result will be unaffected by the yawning of the alligators at the nearby zoo or the onset of an eclipse of the sun. This is what a historian cannot do, for he deals with people and people react unpredictably: nor can we ever know what events are likely to have widespread repercussions.

But how does the scientist decide which factors are important and which can be ignored? Here there may be semantic confusion, for we use the word "important" in two senses which are easily confused.

When he says that a factor is important the scientist usually means that it is a factor about which he can *do* something—he can do his experiment in its presence or absence, or he can alter it in amount. But in everyday life we do not always use the word in this way. When we say that the English Channel has been the most important factor in the political stability of England, we do not envisage the experiment of filling up the channel to confirm that history will now unfold in a different way!

Let us now take an example from physics. A weight falls to the ground and we wish to know why. What is the most important factor which makes it fall? The scientist will say that it is the gravitational pull of the earth. He makes this claim because it is a factor he can alter, and when he does so the rate of fall is changed. For he can drop a weight on a mountain top, or at the bottom of a mine, and on the mountain it falls slower than in the mine. Today he might even try the experiment in a space capsule.

But many other factors might be important too. Do the positions of the earth and the sun in the universe or the galaxy matter?

Would the body fall in the same way if the sun was at the centre of our galaxy, or in one of the spiral arms instead of between them? What would happen if the neutrinos streaming from the sun and stars were cut off, or if the sun itself was captured by a larger star and became a satellite, or if our earth was made of anti-matter instead of ordinary matter? Are the distant galaxies the cause of gravity?[1]—would the weight still fall if they were somehow removed? . . .

In science, speculation which cannot be tested is profitless. So the rule is that if a speculation is beyond possible proof or disproof, it is better not discussed at all. This means that few questions are left for the scientist to ask, and the problems of science become simple enough to be manageable. But in history where great numbers of individuals act and react upon one another, it is impossible to single out one or two of all the causes and to say that all the other possible causes are unimportant. We have already noted how some historians did exactly this in the earlier days and each one thought he had created a science of history. But soon there were many rival systems and no way of deciding between them. One man said this was the law of history, another that. The historian was in the position of the medieval scientist who speculated wildly and interestingly in many directions but did no experiments to see which views were right.

POINTS OF VIEW

The position we reach then is this—that, although there can be no universal science of history, we still need schemes of thought to hold the facts of history together as far as we can. There is no one science of history, but there are or can be *sciences*. In the same way, today, there is no one science of psychology, but there are different psychologies.

It is often useful to write history from a particular point of view. What we must not say is that ours is the only possible point of view. And the same rule, of course, applies in science. If you have successfully accounted for the fall of bodies by gravity, all the facts which have been brought into line may have to be reconsidered in the light of some other principle . . . the viscosity of the

[1] See D. W. S. Sciama, *The Unity of the Universe*, 1959.

air, or the extragalactic nebulae, for example. We can never say for certain that there is one law and only one which will make it possible for us to explain so and so. Indeed, most of the great "break-throughs" in science in recent years have come about because scientists have been prepared to rewrite the "history" of familiar phenomena from new points of view.

But let us return to history. If we take our cue from science the factors which *for us* are important are those about which we can do something. No use looking to the eternal laws of nature as the causes of all events—for we cannot change them. No use dilating upon the interconnectedness or unity of nature—this will not help us.

It is from this point of view that Bible history is written. Why did this or that happen to the chosen nation? Of course there were political reasons, but Israel was small fry, politically speaking, and could do little to change the political situation in other countries. It was better to think of her fortunes in terms of her faithfulness to God. From the time of the Exodus the Hebrews had had good reason to believe that God could manipulate history as He pleased and it was sensible and natural to think of their destiny in these terms. It was a limited view of history, no doubt, but it was relevant and, as we realize today, *all* views are limited, including scientific views.

So the modern approach brings us round full circle to see sense in Hebrew history after all. The disbeliever in Christianity will not agree that God enters into the affairs of a people in the way the Hebrews supposed, but at least all can see that the strangeness of the way in which their history is written is fully justified. And this, as we have pointed out, is the outcome which any Christian would have expected.

CHAPTER 15

PROGRESS, REASON AND PERCEPTION

ALL MEN, BE THEY CHRISTIAN OR OTHERWISE, WISH TO
see society organized in such a way that men can live
together in peace and prosperity. But they often differ about
how this can be achieved.

Science alone cannot provide the answer to this question, yet
science cannot be ignored. Sometimes Christians and non-
Christians, respectively, and in the light of their private convictions
as to the best ways of curing the world's ills, may expect science,
in so far as it relates to human welfare, to develop in different
ways. In this chapter we shall think of some instances of this kind.

MAN'S DOMINION

We may start at an elementary level. Today, no one doubts that
the material welfare of man depends upon a wide-scale application
of science and scientific principles. This was not always so. However, many Christians hold that the enormous possibilities which
are being realized today were foreshadowed in Christian and
Jewish belief. According to the Bible God made man a custodian
of nature: "Fill the earth and subdue it, and have dominion over
the fish of the seas and over the birds of the air and over every
living thing that moveth upon the earth" (*Genesis* 1: 28). It was not
obvious before the days of science that man could ever exert
dominion on this scale, but we are realizing today that the
language is not exaggerated—the physical world *can* be subdued
and even the fish of the sea are in the hand of man. From time to
time Christians have had a vision of the exciting possibilities
ahead[1]—though in past centuries, for example at the time of the

[1] Thus the Nestorian Christian, Job of Edessa (*Book of Treasures*, Baghdad,
A.D. 817—Trans. A. Mingana, Cambridge, 1935, p. 285), in a beautiful passage, speaks of the "ineffable joy" which a knowledge of science ("a perfect
knowledge of the composition of this world . . . etc.") will bring. (Quoted in
full in the present author's *Christian Belief and Science*, p. 36). Early Puritans had
enormous hopes for the future of science.

early Puritans, the vision was followed by disillusionment when it was realized that the task of subduing nature was likely to prove very difficult.

REASON

Turning next to *reason*, it is true that though we cannot *identify* reason with science, the two are nevertheless closely associated in the minds of most people. The success of science is commonly attributed to the disciplined and unfettered use of reason. It is common knowledge, too, that atheists and anti-clerics have commonly espoused the cause of reason, whereas Christians have allowed it more limited scope.

In its day the French Revolution, despite its excesses, was hailed by non-Christian intellectuals as one of the most encouraging events of all time. It was thought to mark the beginning of the end of the old order: the ushering in of the age of Reason and Enlightenment. "I love the generation of the centuries to come," wrote Hölderlin to his brother in 1790 just after the Revolution had begun, "for this is my most blessed hope, the faith which keeps me strong and active, that our grandchildren will be better than we . . . we live in a period of time in which everything is working towards better days."

Similarly, the Revolution led Immanuel Kant to prophesy the "victory of the good principle over the evil, and the establishment of the kingdom of God on earth". The Revolution was the sign that the corrupt version of religion taught by the Churches was on its way out and in its place there would be established pure religious faith or "faith in reason", which was Kant's conception of the Kingdom of God.

In 1792 Kant wrote an essay discussing "whether the human race is continually advancing towards the better". There were three possibilities, he said. The moral standard of humanity might be getting worse, it might be standing still, or it might be getting better. He decided in favour of the third possibility. The first he dismissed out of hand as "a terroristic way of imagining human history" which implied the altogether unthinkable notion that in the end the human race might "blot itself out". He believed himself to have proved "in the strictest theory that the human race has been progressing towards the better and will always continue so to progress". Violence would diminish, men would become law-abiding and would "see themselves obliged first to render the greatest obstacle to morality, namely war, little by little more humane, then less frequent, and finally in the course of time in the shape of aggressive war to abolish it altogether".[1]

The best known apostle of progess was Condorcet (1743–94) who was killed in the Revolution because he was not considered to be revolutionary enough. He had a "fanatical aversion . . . to all religion whatever, and especially to Christianity and Christian institutions". He attempted to predict in detail how man's reason would triumph. Comte, Godwin and others took the same line—for Godwin, the enlightenment of reason would do away with all the ills of life; man had no original sin and, once society was rid of priests, would be free to advance indefinitely.[2] The influence of these and similar writers faded in the second half of the nineteenth century, but Darwinism kept the fervour alive.

For generations the doctrine of progress through Reason has been the faith of rationalism. It is taught that through education men will be taught to reason; the conference table will then replace war, avarice and passion will be tamed and crime recognized as unreasonable. So deep-seated did this faith become that its critics seemed to blaspheme and those whose faith was shattered were profoundly disillusioned—like H. G. Wells who at the last lost faith in any immediate fulfilment of his hopes and spoke of "mind at the end of its tether".

These expectations and hopes were not shared by Christians, with the exception of those who had become so highly secularized in their thinking that they no longer put their Christianity first. According to Christian doctrine war and crime are not to be attributed to lack of education, but to faults of character. Man is not master of his fate: he must accept the free forgiveness and help of God before he can mend his ways.

[1] Passages quoted by J. Pieper, *The End of Time* (Eng. Trans., Faber), 1954. Courtesy of Messrs. Faber & Faber, Ltd.

[2] James Sully's *Pessimism*, 1877, is still a useful reference book on the subject. See also *Enc. Brit.*, etc.

EMPIRICAL TEST OF REASON

A century and a half has passed since the early nineteenth century and it is now possible to judge between secularist and Christian expectations.

At a political and social level there can be little doubt that the non-Christian view has proved wrong. The masses have been educated to an extent far surpassing anything known in previous history, but wars have neither ceased nor become more humane. Increasingly the earth is filled with violence while criminals make good use of their education and intelligence to outwit the police. John Rowland, when a rationalist, made a study of the great criminals of modern history and describes his sense of shock at the discovery that they were often well educated, highly intelligent and originating from a good social background—the opposite of what he had expected to find.[1] Again, Nazism developed in a highly cultured and well-educated country.

In contrast to this, no one who bases his outlook on the New Testament has cause for surprise at the turn of events. The Christian respects reason but keeps a sense of proportion: it is a path towards truth, but *not* the only path. A good intellect is less important than humility, sympathy, contentment, loyalty and desire for truth with a willingness to follow where it leads. In the absence of these, intellect may even prove positively harmful. A study of the origin of inventions and new scientific ideas shows that, very frequently, reason is an impediment, while the exercise of positive faith produces results—as, indeed, any Christian would have expected.[2]

MATHEMATICAL MODEL

There is another assumption which seems to lie at the basis of secularist thinking which, again, the Christian does not share.

It is likely that, consciously or otherwise, Kant and others of his persuasion took mathematical thinking as the model for all thinking. The mathematician who tells you what he is assuming—his axioms—can then prove his proposition in such a way that, if you

[1] John Rowland, *A Century of Murder*, 1950; *One Man's Mind*, 1952, p. 97.
[2] R. E. D. Clark, *Christian Belief and Science* (English University Press), 1960.

can think at all, you must in the end agree with him. His reasoning is rigid and inexorable—at least in so far as it *is* reason. (We may ignore intuitional methods in mathematics as being outside the scope of reason—they would certainly have been considered so until recently.)

Reason, then, is taken to be a certain and reliable process. Provided our minds are working properly, and we have been properly trained in the use of language, we may be sure that if we are supplied with the same facts we shall reach the same conclusion as our neighbour.

It is only against a background of this kind that we can appreciate the appeal of the age of Reason. Train the mind of the criminal and he will see at once that it is unreasonable to steal: education will ensure that all trouble-makers in society will mend their ways. The assumption is that if I can see that so and so is illogical, then you and everyone else will see it too. Just as there can be no question of the same axioms leading one person to assert that the law of Pythagoras is true and another to assert that it is false, so there can be no question of those whose conduct depends on reason behaving some in one way and some in another.

Again, this teaching runs contrary to the teaching of the New Testament. Dives wants to return to the land of the living to warn his relations of what lies beyond, but is told that if they will not hear Moses and the prophets, neither will they be convinced if one rises from the dead. This question of evidence arises repeatedly in the New Testament. Again and again the point is made that it is sometimes wrong to give people too much evidence, for in sheer perversity they may react against the truth. For this reason some of those who are cured by Jesus are told to keep the fact secret, demons are told not to make Christ known, those who seek a sign from heaven are told that no sign will be given to that generation, and disciples are told not to give pearls to pigs!

Once again, then, we recognize two differing outlooks: once again they lead us to expect different results. To the first question, Does education make men good? we have already noted that modern history has provided an answer. We now see that this is linked with the further question, Does psychology confirm that, given the same premises, two people will reach the same conclusion?

PERCEPTION

Turning to this second question, let us consider the facts. In recent years the study of perception has been much to the fore. The fear has been expressed that, because millions of people see the same television programmes, individuality will be stamped out. But psychologists who have studied the matter find that the same programme is seen in different ways by different people. There is a brawl between a son and his parents: some see it as a row between a good lad and his bad parents, some between a bad lad and his good parents, some between a bad lad and his bad parents. The morals drawn by those who see and hear the same sights and sounds are not at all the same.

Much work has been done in the field of illusions. If we look at Figure 1 (the Necker cube) it may appear as a box if looked at from a position slightly above, or as a cube if looked at from slightly below the level of the object. But as we look at it, one perception changes over into the other, then back again, and the reversals continue so long as we look at the figure.

Now the extraordinary thing is that although we see two *different* things, though not both at once, the image that is thrown on the retina is exactly the same in the two cases. The same nerve fibres are stimulated, the same messages travel to the brain. Yet we do not always see the same thing.[1]

Are we *interpreting* what we see? Certainly not consciously. We do not see a number of lines on the paper and ask how they should be interpreted. Yet in some way the mind organizes what we see. Seeing, then, does not consist only in the fact that an image is thrown upon the retina of the eye and sends a message back to the brain. At different moments we may receive the same message from the outer world, yet see different things. And if this happens to you or me, and if only a few moments may make all the difference to *what* we see, then we may be sure that two persons given the same facts will not always understand them in the same way.

Though some figures switch backwards and forwards from one appearance to another, this does not always happen. Take Figure 2, for instance. We may see it as a bird facing to the left, or as an

[1] See Professor Hanson's useful discussion on this subject of which free use has been made above. N. R. Hanson, *Patterns of Discovery*, 1958, Chapter 1.

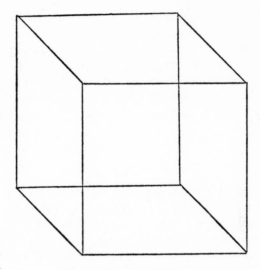

Fig. 1. The Necker Cube

Fig. 2. Bird facing to the left, or antelope facing to the right?
(After Hanson)

antelope facing to the right. When once we have seen it in one form or the other the chances are that unless our attention is drawn to it, we shall not notice the second possibility. This illustrates a general principle of psychology, which applies to animals as well as men. Apes which have learned to solve a problem in one way find it unusually difficult to learn another; rats which have learned to escape from a maze along a particular route find it difficult to recognize a different but equally easy way of escape. When once an insight has been gained, our minds are in some way blocked so that it is now harder to view the situation in a different light.

CONTEXT

How then can we make someone see what he cannot see for himself? We can often do this by supplying context. If we draw the rest of the bird (or part of it), on the one hand, or of the antelope on the other, then there will be no doubt what is intended. Octopuses eat crabs which crawl along the sea bed, but if a crab is held high in the water, an octopus does not recognize it as a crab at all, even if he is hungry. To make him see it as a crab we must supply the correct background. The dull student in an examination does not recognize that the question he cannot answer is one he has often answered before in another connexion.

It seems that it is this principle which so often makes it difficult to communicate our thoughts to others. Not only do we not know how they will view facts which seem important to us, but we do not know what kind of a context would be necessary for them to appreciate things as we do.

RESTORED SIGHT

Another line of inquiry concerns those who were born blind but who later received sight as a result of an operation. When sight is first gained, the sensation of colourful patterns which the rest of us call "seeing" conveys no meaning at first. Those born blind lack a sense of distance or depth and so do not realize that objects which are near will appear larger than those which are far away. The world appears flat and for this reason Necker cubes and similar figures show no reversals. Confusions are so great that today, as in the Gospel story, objects as different as trees and men may be confused.[1] A patient may be so bewildered by the gift of sight that he may wish, at first, that he had remained blind.

Again, we draw the conclusion that in the ordinary act of seeing the mind is very active indeed, imposing interpretations on the messages which are received by the eye. But it is an unconscious process—in the ordinary way we cannot analyse or even know what we are doing. In the same way reasoning and education are meaningless to us except in so far as our minds unconsciously force the facts into grooves of thought without our being aware of the fact. Christians have always held that this is so, but have added that the interpretations which the mind imposes often depend on moral issues—upon whether in the last resort we *want* to do right or to do wrong, to accept truth and recognize our errors or to justify ourselves. This Christian view does not seem to have been tested experimentally, though it is very reasonable and can be seen to operate in everyday life. The Christian would expect that when psychologists come to test the effects of moral issues on perception they will find them of importance.

INSANITY

The study of insanity in recent times has also thrown much further light on perception. It used to be supposed that insane people had diseased minds and were incapable of logical reasoning. But this is rarely so. In *paranoia* the patient is highly intelligent, often more so than an average person. Yet he perceives the data which come to him from the outside world in a curiously distorted way. His mind twists the most ordinary happenings so that they add to the sum-total of the evidence that he is being persecuted. If people treat him roughly it confirms persecution; if in a friendly way it is because they desire to gain his confidence to take advantage of him at a later date. If people laugh they laugh at him; if they talk they are hatching their plots; if they are silent it is because they do not

[1] M. von Senden, *Space and Sight*, 1960; R. E. D. Clark, "Men as Trees Walking", *Faith and Thought* (Victoria Institute), 1963, **93**, 88. The possibility of this confusion, confirmed by von Senden, follows naturally if we accept the Gospel record.

wish him to hear what they are planning, Against this fortress reason is powerless. Tell him that he imagines the persecution and he thinks you are seeking to put him off his guard—perhaps you are even in the enemy's pay.

In *schizophrenia* (split-mindedness) there are alternate moods of extreme happiness and abject depression. But the mind works rationally all the time, though in the depressive state symbolism becomes highly important. A door opening and closing becomes a symbol of a demon whose mouth will open and close to devour you; the ill omen of a clap of thunder will fill you with terror; towels and cloths may appear as devils to which you give names.

Communication with schizophrenics has always been extremely difficult. They sense that we do not talk their language and cannot imagine how they feel. But dosed with drugs such as mescaline or the much more potent LSD 25 a normal person becomes insane for around a day and thereafter can often understand patients who suffer permanently in this way. The fascinating point emerges that the messages received through the senses are actually altered under the influence of drugs. The alcoholic may see pink rats but these are imaginary: the taker of mind-affecting (psychomimetic) drugs will see what is really there, but see it differently. A man may be seen quite clearly, but with his head attached upside down; objects become surrounded with brilliant colours; distortions of sights and sounds give them a new and usually false significance.

These extraordinary changes, caused by the presence of minute traces of chemicals in the brain, make it likely that even in normal people there are wide variations in the way we see, hear and feel. And the extreme difficulty of using reason usefully with mental defectives suggests that the same difficulty, though less extreme, will be found between otherwise normal people. For we always observe *extreme* differences first (e.g. hot and cold, high and low) and only realize later that they often merge into one another. In the same way it is now generally conceded that sanity and insanity are not sharply divided—"we are all a little touched!"

Again, then, science is making it clear that intellectual approaches to problems may not always be the best way to achieve co-operation. The conference table may accentuate rather than remove causes of friction. Intellectuals in the West can produce a cast-iron argument that over-population is an imminent danger to the world: in underdeveloped countries it is widely suspected that propaganda for population control, coming from the West, is a new and sinister weapon for exterminating the black races. It is not easy to allay suspicions of this kind.

CONCLUSION

Thus the general outcome of research in several directions—the study of crime, of perception in psychology, of insanity and of the action of psychomimetic drugs—all point in a direction which does not surprise the Christian but is certainly contrary to the expectations of the humanists of the past. To some, such results may seem unduly gloomy and likely to lead to despair. If problems cannot be solved by reason will they ever be solved? But this outlook is misguided. We place too much emphasis on intellect. It is not the people with the best arguments who can most effectively influence their fellows, but those who can inspire trust—a very different matter. The traditional Christian virtues are of more value than a high I.Q.; a society which rates them lower must take the consequences.

At the same time, it ill becomes a Christian to disparage reason: indeed, those who do so are inconsistent for they seek to establish their case by reason. Reason is one of the best tools for finding truth, but it is not the only tool and it is not infallible. Rightly used, according to the Bible, it will lead men to God, bringing them to that frame of mind in which they can recognize God's revelation.

CHAPTER 16

MORE ABOUT BEGINNINGS

IN AN EARLIER CHAPTER (CHAPTER 4) WE DISCUSSED the supposed "gap" in our knowledge about the beginning of the universe. We found good reason for denying that there is any risk whatsoever that this "gap" might one day "close up", so "squeezing" God out of His universe and replacing Him by scientific laws!

There are other "gaps" of a similar kind which also relate to beginnings—of the earth, of life, of biological species and of man —and these, like the one we considered, have often given rise to controversies in which atheists and Christians have taken opposite sides. They, too, call for comment.

The complexities of the problems involved in all discussions of beginnings are so great, and the times at which events happened so remote, that it cannot yet be expected that science will come forward with ready-made answers—if, indeed, this will ever be possible. Nevertheless, the scientific and Christian evidence, so far as it goes, is of great interest and it is often possible to discern trends of scientific thinking at the present time. In this and the following chapter we shall therefore attempt to treat of these matters briefly as well as to make a few further comments on the subject of cosmogony to complete the picture.

In discussing Christian points of view it is well at the start to be clear concerning the difficulties that lie ahead. On the one hand the stories about origins in the Bible are necessarily written in extremely old and primitive language, composed at a time when words had not the definite meanings that they later came to possess. Words like *made, day, created, all* (in, *all* the earth covered by the flood), *earth* (=land—local?), *high mountains* (=highest of the local hills?) might all be taken by a later generation in a more definite and restricted sense than had been intended—with the result that theologians of the past were too apt to give a more dogmatic picture of what the Bible taught than could be justified. Similarly, on the scientific side, the questions asked are difficult and our knowledge about the past still very limited. A good deal of uncertainty and many unsolved problems are therefore inevitable.

CREATION

According to Christian theology, God created the heaven and the earth. We cannot be *quite* sure that the Hebrew words used in *Genesis* mean that the universe was created out of nothing, rather than fashioned out of some pre-existent chaotic material, but the former view is usually held by Jews and Christians.

If we accept the creation of the universe, it is natural to suppose that, being a created thing, it is finite rather than infinite. If this seems inconclusive, the Christian will at least reflect that the finiteness of the cosmos is supported by the Biblical statement that God humbles himself to behold things in heaven[1], and again that the heaven of heavens cannot contain God.[2]

Christian theology seems to be committed to the view that the universe was created in time, though not necessarily suddenly. Perhaps this implies that time itself was in some way created, or had a start, though this again does not necessarily follow. What does seem certain is that because there was a creation epoch at the beginning, the way in which God worked at the time is not the same as the way He works—or usually works—today. Thus the Bible teaches that "things which are seen were not made of things which do appear"[3] and it stresses the point that God "rested" after He had created, which certainly implies that He ceased to act as He had done before.[4] Since the universe is no longer being created it is subject to decay. For this reason it becomes possible to contrast God with his universe—the heavens wax old like a garment but God remains the same from age to age.[5]

Here Christian doctrine is quite contrary to atheistic opinion. We have seen that atheists like to toy with the idea that the universe is eternal and we may note that this, together with the theory that

[1] *Psalm* 113: 6.
[2] *Chronicles* 6: 18.
[3] *Hebrews* 11: 3.
[4] *Genesis* 2: 23; *Exodus* 20: 11; 31: 17; *Hebrews* 4: 4.
[5] *Psalm* 102; 25–26; *Hebrews* 1: 10–11.

the universe is also infinite, are considered as basic postulates of atheistic Marxism.

SCIENCE COMPATIBLE WITH CREATION

How do these conjectures stand in the light of modern astronomy? We have already noted (Chapter 4) that evidence is accumulating in favour of a creation epoch, behind which it is impossible for science to probe. This is what a Christian, accepting creation, would expect to find but it is contrary to the expectations of atheism.

Science is compatible with—in fact highly suggestive of—the Christian doctrine of creation. But in the strict sense it can only lead us back to a scientific *impasse*, at which point it seems highly reasonable to introduce a new and non-scientific way of thinking. The best explanation we can offer to "explain" (in the sense of "throw light on" or "bring the facts together to make them seem less strange") the universe is to suppose that it was planned by a Master Mind. It is difficult to avoid this conclusion, though equally difficult to develop it in the way that scientific ideas are usually developed.

The argument that this line of thought puts a stop to thinking is one which we have already examined (p. 25). Here we may merely note that since there must be limits in any case, and since the limit must be reached at *some* point, why should it not come here?

In arguing in this way, we invoke no new or unfamiliar way of thinking. In ordinary life we look for scientific causes so long as we can, but when the limit comes we cheerfully pass on to consider causes of other kinds. We say an instrument was *planned* by an engineer, or that some factor such as, say, *devotion*, made a man act in the way he did. Explanations of this kind—and psychoanalysis also uses them freely—may be quite reasonable, but they are outside the field of strict science and they are always dead ends to thought. We cannot go further and decide *how* a man planned an instrument, or discover, by analysis what devotion or the Oedipus complex is made of! Nor can we usually do experiments to test these theories. It would seem, then, that this objection is not a valid one for rejecting the idea of God as Creator.

FINITE OR INFINITE

Is the universe *finite or infinite*? It is fair to say that most of the work covering the past half-century has favoured the view that it is finite. Einstein's space, for instance, is finite though unbounded and Eddington believed that he could calculate the total number of particles in the universe.

Until recently the steady state theory of the universe, which favoured the infinite view, had some following, but it has become increasingly difficult to reconcile it with the facts of astronomy and it has been abandoned by Hoyle, its best-known advocate. Since the early 1960's the theories of elementary particles have suggested that space-time is finite and it is interesting to note that this has caused embarrassment in Russia.[1] The theory of an expanding universe formed from a primeval fire-ball also suggests a finite universe.

On the whole, then, we may say that science favours a finite universe. But the subject is difficult, and in cosmology new views are put forward so frequently that it would be hazardous to be dogmatic.

Most Christians will probably expect that the present view will turn out to be correct—though it is no part of the Christian faith to assert dogmatically that an infinite universe is impossible. "I remember," says Descartes, "that the Cardinal of Cusa and several other Doctors have supposed the world infinite, without having ever been reproved by the Church on this subject; on the contrary, it is believed that to conceive His works very great is to honour God."[2]

SEEDS OF DECAY

Now let us turn to the Christian doctrine that there are seeds of decay in the natural order. In the 1930's the doctrine of the heat death of the universe received much attention but it is less often discussed today. Those who argue that the universe is infinite naturally hold that it is impossible to jump from the conclusion that the principle of increasing entropy (or *disorder* understood in

[1] *Studies in Soviet Thought*, 1964, 4, 296.
[2] *Oeuvres*, V, 19; quoted, A. Koyré, op. cit. p. 194.

a special sense) which applies to finite quantities of matter cannot be applied to an infinite cosmos. But the principle seems to be sound enough and is, as Eddington pointed out long ago, intimately connected with the fact that time is not reversible. We need not be too concerned with heat as such—there are many ways in which arrangement or order can break down in the course of time other than by a fall in the availability of heat for doing work. We may perhaps connect entropy in its wider sense with the expansion of the universe which seems to suggest that matter is becoming progressively more scattered as we get farther away in time from an original creation epoch. It is fair then to conclude that science strongly favours the view that nature contains its own seeds of decay. This is, in fact, another form of the law, considered earlier, that nature abhors the long arm of coincidence. If highly improbable coincidence occurs, then self-ordering rather than the reverse will take place (as we saw in Chapter 4), and science will be impossible.

The mere fact that in science we look for the causes of *order* rather than of *disorder*, assumes that order needs explaining: that it does *not* arise spontaneously. Explanation consists in relating it to some other form of order, often invisible, which, in the process of degrading, produces visible ordered phenomena. This principle lies at the basis of science: once it is questioned, the door is left open to superstitions of every kind—spontaneous generation explains the origin of every unexpected animal: natural ordering forces explain why rocks are sometimes shaped like fossils; vital forces and entelechies explain how food is converted into human flesh. . . . Science is at an end.

THE EARTH

Jews and Christians have always thought that the earth was prepared by God in some special way as a home for life, or at least for human life. In the old days this view fitted in well with the Ptolemaic system of astronomy, according to which the earth was situated at the centre of the universe, but it was not dependent upon this view. But atheists never had reason for thinking that the earth was especially privileged.

With the discovery at the beginning of the modern era that the

earth is not at the centre of the solar system after all, Christianity
suffered a serious reverse at the hands of science. Roman Catholic
opposition to Galileo underlined the defeat in the popular mind
and subsequent discoveries have emphasized the smallness of the
earth in the scheme of things. Historically this is probably the
most striking instance that can be given of the failure of the religious and the success of the non-religious anticipations about the
course of scientific discovery—to many people it still seems to
prove that Christianity backs the losing horse!

The subject has been discussed endlessly—there is no space
here for more than brief comments.

Firstly, we should try to understand the older Christian view.
Christians believed then, as they still believe today, that the earth is
privileged in some way. Now astronomers, over many centuries,
had taught that the earth was situated at the centre of the universe,
so it was natural enough for Christians to link their faith with
this supposed fact. Ordinary people were hardly in a position to
discover that the sun and not the earth was at the centre of the
solar system!

It is sometimes suggested that the new views might have been
more readily accepted if Christians had not lined their faith with
their science in this way. But this is doubtful, to say the least, for
it is now common knowledge that Galileo advanced some highly
fallacious arguments in support of his new system of astronomy.
To suggest that an older generation of Christians did wrong to
link the current belief about the earth's place in the scheme of
things with the best scientific knowledge of the day is to be un-
realistic, as, indeed, we have already had cause to note. Such a
policy would inevitably have encouraged a dichotomy of mind
and killed the cross-fertilization of ideas between philosophy and
religion on the one hand and science on the other—to the detri-
ment of both. When we hold different but rather similar ideas in
different contexts we cannot help wondering if they are connected.
We must always try to make our thinking a unity – if we make
mistakes we must not give up the attempt but try again.

What lessons may we draw then from the geocentric-heliocen-
tric controversy? They are four-fold. First, that Christians, being
only men, can make mistakes; second, that we must be willing to
change our minds in the face of new evidence; third, that we need

to delve more deeply into what it is that as Christians we believe—a divine favour bestowed upon the earth need not necessarily take the form of making it the centre of the universe!—and, fourth, that we should not put all our eggs into one basket. The last point implies that we must look for agreement (or disagreement) in hundreds of instances rather than in one or two: the believer who does this will not be unduly upset if on occasion things do not turn out as he expects. These are also the conclusions we have reached in other connexions. Yet in the present instance we may willingly concede that the discovery that the earth goes round the sun is a case in which Christian expectation proved wrong.

What is the position today? Are there grounds for thinking that the earth is unique—or at least highly privileged? The question is not *necessarily* concerned with astronomy. If, as Christians believe, this earth was visited by Christ, the unique ("only-begotten") incarnation of God, then it is privileged indeed. Nevertheless, a Christian might reasonably hazard a guess that the earth would be privileged in other ways too—though he could hardly on Christian grounds say what such grounds might be.

Astronomy, in modern times, has underlined the fact that the earth is remarkable in fulfilling the requirements of a planet where life can exist; no other body in the solar system comes near to it in this respect. Even Mars, which at one time was confidently held to be the home of advanced forms of life, turned out to be a dry, very hot planet, rather like the moon in appearance, when photographed by Mariner IV. It might sustain very lowly forms of plant life, but according to present evidence this does not seem likely.

What about the rest of the universe? May it not contain vast numbers of habitable planets such as ours? To answer this we should need to know how planets are formed. If they are formed as a result of excessively rare events, such as, for instance, near encounters of stars, they may be very rare in the universe: if, on the other hand, they are produced as a result of common occurrences, say by the condensation of matter in space, they may be quite common. Present views, mainly favour the second alternative, but they are influenced—and the admission is often quite open—by what those who hold them would *like* to be true, rather than by any finding of science. Despite dogmatism—more particularly in Russia—we just do not know.

EARTH'S EARLIEST AGES

Whatever view we take of the origin of the earth, the story of the ocean will probably be much the same, save perhaps for differences in the time-scale involved.

If the earth was formed hot from the substance of a star, then, as it cooled, the water dissolved in the rocks must have boiled out as they solidified. If the earth was formed cold from meteoric matter, then it must have heated up radioactively at a later stage— ensured by the abundance of the radioactive forms of potassium and uranium a few thousand million years ago—until all or some part was molten, when ocean water would have been expelled as before. (Water is quite soluble in molten rocks, and steam, not derived from the sea, is still emitted by volcanoes.) In any case there is no doubt that much of the crust of the earth was once in a molten condition.

The story of the early stages of the earth's formation is told in the first chapter of *Genesis* and in the thirty-eighth chapter of *Job*. The agreement with modern views is remarkable. Potentially Christians have long been in a position to predict the course of scientific discovery regarding the early history of the earth.

We are told that the ocean "burst forth from the womb"— an apt metaphor. When the earth's surface was hot, some or all of the ocean must have been in the form of steam, which would have shielded the earth from the sun's rays, so that "there was darkness over the face of the deep". Under the great pressure caused by hot vapours above, so-called "critical" conditions would have been reached so that at first there would be no distinction between vapour and liquid. Later, as the temperature fell, the water and the vapour just above it would have had almost equal densities, so that gravity would have little effect in keeping the water in its place and tides caused by the moon or in other ways would have taken the form of gigantic waves circumnavigating the earth. (The "Spirit of God moved upon the face of the waters" says *Genesis*—implying great motion as a physical concomitant:

"mighty wind" is also a legitimate alternative translation: "proud waves" in *Job*.)

As condensation proceeded, diffuse light must have percolated through the clouds, and in time day and night were distinguishable, though the sun and moon would not at first be visible. Later there must have been a time when the mists rose, forming clear sky between the liquid water below and the cloud cover above—the clear sky being the "firmament" ("God called the firmament heaven", i.e. *sky*) When precipitation had become virtually complete, the continents would drain giving the dry land, and plants would appear. According to *Genesis* this happened before the clouds had cleared sufficiently for sun, moon and stars to be visible from the surface of the earth, which seems reasonable.

We assume that the account is written from the point of view of an imaginary observer on the earth, as this seems the most natural way in which a revelation of how the earth had come to exist would have been given to early man.

The suggestion that the revelation was made in a series of visions given at night ("the evening and the morning were the . . . day") has much in its favour.[1] It has been criticized on the ground that in *Exodus* chapter 20 we are told that it was in six days that the Lord *made* heaven and earth, not that they were revealed in six days. But *made* here may again be from man's point of view. If this be so, we may read the words in the sense—"as seen by the man to whom the Lord revealed the story of creation, the Lord made heaven and earth in six days". The emphasis, of course, is on God's *work*, the fact that he had *made* the world in stages, not on the relatively trivial point that He had taken six days to reveal how He did it.

This is not a forced interpretation because there is little doubt that much of the Bible is written from *man's* point of view—indeed, it is difficult to see how revelation could be given in any other way. We have a close parallel in, for example, the statement that it was on the fourth day that God *made* the sun, moon and stars, for this cannot mean that there had been no sun before this time. Even the most primitive savage would have known that day and night are connected with sunrise and sunset, even when the sky is cloudy, so he would not have supposed that there could be day

[1] P. J. Wiseman, *Creation Revealed in Six Days*, 1948.

and night before the creation of the sun. We must understand the statement in the sense, "From man's point of view, it was on the fourth day that God made the sun . . .". The same principle would apply all through *Genesis*, chapter 1. For instance it is the teeming of the waters with fish life which would have been noticed as a feature of the fifth day, but there is no clear statement as to when the first forms of life were present in the waters.

On this view, it is reasonable to interpret the days of *Genesis* quite literally, even though they stand (as Augustine said long ago) for geological periods of unspecified length.

There are some difficulties in *Genesis* 1 relating to the order in which some of the forms of life appeared. But there is little certainty as to the meaning of some of the terms used and sensible (if unproven) suggestions can be made which will bring the account into line with the geological record. The creation of Eve also poses a problem. But notwithstanding difficulties, a Christian may feel that considerable harmony has been achieved.

CHAPTER 17

LIFE, EARLY MAN AND NOAH'S FLOOD

LIFE

CHRISTIANS HAVE USUALLY SUPPOSED THAT GOD created at least some forms of life in the early ages of the earth, though the Bible does not definitely make it clear whether God's activity involved miracles or whether He worked by natural means. (This belief must not be confused with the doctrine of the special creation of species which, once they had been created, were supposed not to be capable of transformation from one into another. The theory of the fixity of species was not held in the Middle Ages and only held sway for a relatively short period before Darwin, when it was based on scientific not theological reasoning.) Atheists, on the other hand, disbelieving in the possibility of miracles, have always said that life must have arisen by natural processes from non-living matter.

Again, the problem has not been finally settled: indeed, since the idea of creation does not lie within the province of science, no final decision *on scientific grounds* is possible. At best, science might reach an *impasse*. The scientific arguments which bear on the problem are as follows.

Many of the simpler compounds which are found in living matter can by synthesized by man and we can dimly imagine— though the time is very far distant—that man might one day arrange synthetic compounds in such a way as to make an object alike in all respects, so far as *physical* structure goes, to a living organism. Whether such an object would be alive or not we do not know. It may well be that psychic factors about which we know nothing would have to be placed in the object as well as chemical molecules to make it alive.

Let us suppose, however, that the object turned out to be alive. The total amount of human effort and thought entailed in this feat— for each scientist in the chain has available all the published human knowledge that went before—would be prodigious. Though a materialist might hail such a synthesis as proof of a materialistic view of the origin of life, a Christian might with more justice claim that intelligence comparable with the vast accumulation of human wisdom must have existed *before* there was any life on earth, otherwise the first living cells could hardly have been formed at all.

The non-Christian attitude has gained some ground in recent years in that it has led to the successful prediction that certain organic compounds might be synthesized in a simple way. This has been done by mixing together such inorganic chemicals (H_2O, CO_2, NH_3, CH_4, etc.) as might be expected to exist on the surface of a primitive planet, and subjecting the mixture to ultra-violet light or electric discharge. In this way it has been found that a number of simple amino acids and simple cyclic compounds (including those containing pyrimidine and pyrazole rings) are formed in small quantities, together with many other products. This is not really surprising, for to be viable organisms must be built around a nexus of the most stable units possible—and thermodynamics demands that the most stable systems will be formed when chemical species are made to react with one another under extreme conditions. Nevertheless, it is a fact that the discovery arose as a result of atheistic thinking.

To continue, even the simplest form of life involves a balance between the activities of hundreds or probably thousands of enzymes catalysing a great many reactions: it involves the presence of extremely unstable molecular systems which exist at all only because they are resynthesized as fast as they decompose: it also involves mechanisms for the self-duplication of the entire system. Despite some very "iffy" suggestions, no acceptable theory as to how, in principle, the simplest self-duplicating cell could have come into existence in the first place is forthcoming as yet, and the difficulties which such a theory would have to meet have grown steadily in recent years.[1]

Finally, the quite staggering complexity of life—to be contrasted with the extreme simplicity of the "protoplasm" envisaged by atheistic writers in the nineteenth century—is highly suggestive of an Intelligence at the back of the universe. The argument is equally cogent whether we suppose that matter contains in itself the degree of complexity necessary so that life will come into

[1] M. Dixon and E. C. Webb, *Enzymes*, 2nd ed. 1964, pp. 665 ff.

being when conditions are right, or whether we imagine that God intervened from time to time in a direct way. Life is a surprising thing to emerge from matter—as J. D. Bernal candidly confesses, "It would be easier to discuss how life didn't originate than how it did"[1]—and it is hard to divorce it from the idea of careful planning at least at some stage. Many Christians will feel that it may be easier to suppose that God intervened in the earth's history than to encase the difficulties in the structure of matter itself. Is the object of the latter procedure, they wonder, to put the difficulties safely out of sight? As Dixon and Webb remark, those who, like Oparin in Russia, put forward schemes for biosynthesis, do so without much appreciation of the difficulties involved.

These comments on the origin of life are to a large extent also applicable to the subject of evolution. Here again it is *possible* that natural laws have brought into being the wonderful variety of life what we see around us. Certainly it does not seem difficult to understand that species built on the same general plan might transform, but where more radical changes are involved the difficulties become vastly greater. There appears to be a growing feeling, even among those who accept evolution unreservedly, that natural selection which starts with a single form of life, is inadequate to account for nature as we find it.[2] But the difficulties associated with discovering a better theory are very great indeed, and despite much materialistic dogmatism, it is not evident that we are any nearer to a scientific solution of the problem.

ORIGIN OF MAN

Until modern times, most people believed, on what they took to be "biblical authority", that man had existed on earth for only a few thousand years and that his forebears had been specially created by God. In the second half of the nineteenth century science seemed to prove that both these beliefs were false. The unearthing of prehistoric human bones, and the theory of evolution, respectively, seemed to show that man was exceedingly old and that he

[1] British Broadcasting Corporation, 3rd Programme, 9 March 1959.
[2] See, for example, G. A. Kerkut, op. cit. who insists that the evidence points to a number of separate starting points. Also, Sir Alister Hardy, *The Living Stream,* 1965.

was descended from animals. The discoveries of science were not at all in keeping with Christian anticipations.

Let us look at the problem again in the light of more recent thought. On the biblical side, it is now widely felt that the claim that man is descended from the apes, or a common ancestor of both apes and man, is not definitely denied in the Bible, in so far as man's *body* is concerned. It is possible to read the words, "Let us make man in our image . . ." in the sense, "Let us make the already existing species man into a being with our image . . .". There is no need to identify the tool-making man of prehistory who may be traced back for nearly two million years, with man in the image of God.

But what about the Biblical date for man? Here research is beginning to vindicate the original Christian expectations. It is agreed that technology and agriculture arose first of all in the countries of the Middle East at about the Biblical date. This was the time when man first began to multiply and to show his power as lord of creation. From that time until today civilizations have flourished and declined and, with the exception of small isolated units, man has been in a process of constant change socially and technologically. History, in fact, seems to start only at around 8–10,000 B.C., near the close of the last Ice Age. Before that there are isolated and very small communities, able to make very simple tools such as flints and sometimes to paint pictures on walls of caves—but there is no evidence that they existed in large numbers, or that they were outstandingly inventive (even animals show *some* inventiveness). In hundreds of thousands, even millions, of years, they learned little more than how to shape arrow-heads and make primitive shelters. Even the simplest conceptions, like that of the wheel, or the deliberate growing of food for future use (achieved even by the social insects) seem to have been beyond them.

Thus archaeology seems to confirm the Biblical teaching that something new and remarkable happened in the Middle East around 8–10,000 B.C. The common view is that man then began to settle down to a settled community existence based on agriculture.[1]

---

[1] There is no *proof* that modern man is connected with pre-Adamite man. So far as science can tell us, early man *might* have died out, and modern man *might* have been introduced at a later stage by creation—or, as some might prefer, by flying saucers from another planet! Most people reject this view because it invokes an unverified hypothesis, but it *could* be true.

A further interesting possibility is that he then, for the first time, began to make use of language—a suggestion now taken seriously by secular authorities,[1] and fully compatible with the view that, at the Biblical date, God gave to man a new nature conferring on him a god-like quality of mind and fitting him to take dominion over the earth. It may well be that with the dawning sense of responsibility and awareness of what he could become, there came also the knowledge of good and evil.

THE UNIQUENESS OF MAN

Christians have always believed that man is unique for he was specially made by God and, in God's view, was worth redeeming when he became a sinner. If this be so, then we should expect science to reveal features of man which show him to be unique. On the other hand, the traditional secular view sees in man a glorified monkey of little cosmic significance.

The earlier rationalists indulged in violent controversy in their attempts to prove that man was an animal—though a clever one —but nothing more. Huxley for example was concerned to show that every structure in man's anatomy was present in that of the ape. (More recent work has shown that there are definite anatomical differences—especially in the brain.[2])

Discussion of the uniqueness of man raises two separate questions. Firstly, is man unique among animals and, secondly, is he unique in the cosmos?

That man differs from the animals in some way seems clear enough. Even Julian Huxley, a humanist, entitles one of his books, *The Uniqueness of Man*—a title which would have seemed out of place on a secular bookshelf in the nineteenth century!

However, it is surprisingly difficult to nail down in words what it is that makes man unique. Small (or apparently small) anatomical differences may or may not be significant. As for mental differences, glimmerings of rational thought, conscience, loyalty to the group, unselfishness, ability to appreciate numbers up to about 15 (though not, it seems, to count them), desire for private property, use of

[1] R. Paget (Sir) *Nature*, 1945, **156**, 209, suggests 4–6000 B.C. for the beginning of language. See also W. M. S. Russell, *The Listener*, 12 November 1964, p. 753.

[2] See especially, F. W. Jones, *Hallmarks of Mankind*, 1948.

language or its equivalent, ability to draw, paint, use tools and so on, are certainly to be found in the animal creation. It may be that thinking in words—distinct concepts which can be strung together intelligently to convey a seemingly infinite variety of meanings—is a distinguishing feature, but the Christian holds that there must be a spiritual factor too. Even if this is largely inaccessible to science, it is reasonable to think that science will ultimately learn something about it—or at least that it exists. We cannot say what the final outcome will be, but no development of recent science leads us to doubt that Christians have been right in stressing man's uniqueness among other forms of life. Even at its lowest level few doubt that man is unique in his ability to wonder why he is here and how the universe came into being.

One factor, which may be extremely significant, is the quite extraordinary lack of psychical manifestations amongst animals. When we remember that, apart from natural encounters with wild beasts, thousands of millions of animals must have been reared on farms or as pets, and multitudes more venerated as sacred like the cat in ancient Egypt or the cow in India, how is it that we never hear of haunted dog-kennels, sheep which levitate or poltergeists which require the presence of a female piglet? Though these weird happenings are very rare among humans, so rare that they are often doubted, yet they do seem to be connected with some characteristically human phenomenon. It seems very strange that these phenomena (or even reasonably convincing *rumours* of these phenomena) are confined to the human species. An expert who has spent a lifetime collecting and studying curious information of this kind once told the author that he had never encountered a single case connected with an animal which was worth investigating.[1] This fact alone, whatever its significance may be, would seem to indicate that there is a difference between man and beast—a difference in *kind*, not merely in degree.

MAN IN THE COSMOS

Reiterated talk of scientists listening for communications from unknown creatures in outer space, coupled with a plethora of

[1] E. J. Dingwall. See *Science and Religion*, 1948, 1, 35.

science-fiction novels, may give the impression that science supports the view that the universe is fairly thickly peopled with folk
like ourselves! Of this there is no evidence whatever.

Man is but one of many millions of past and present species,
yet he is the only one able to think rationally about the universe
in which he lives. And though the earth has been here for several
thousand million years, civilized man has existed for but a few
millionth parts of the total period and for only a small fraction of
this time again has he known how to make more than trivial use
of the forces of nature around him.

Let it be supposed that there are a great number of planets in
the universe on which man *could* live. If this be so, then from what
we have said we should hardly expect one in a million, perhaps
one in a million million, to be inhabited by man-like beings at the
present time.

The feeling that the man in the street has been far too ready to
believe in an inhabited universe is now growing among seriously-
minded biologists. If, as is commonly assumed, man is a product of
evolution, then (so it is argued) we can obtain some idea of the
probability of his emergence from a study of his evolutionary
history. The probability turns out to be very low indeed. Again
and again, on hundreds, perhaps thousands, of occasions, just the
right thing happened. Often man's line might have died out as did
countless other lines, but it continued despite poor survival value
and low numbers. The argument that geological time is so long
anyway that there was plenty of time for unlikely things to happen,
is not weighty. It was necessary for them to happen *at the right
time* and "chances once missed were not likely to recur. . . . Geological time may be long but it is short in comparison with the
improbability (in the statistical sense) of the sequence of accidents"
required (Sandon). The idea that there are other beings in the
universe like ourselves with whom we ought to be able to
communicate is judged by such prominent biologists as G. G.
Simpson as "plainly false" and by E. B. Ford as "incredibly improbable". Professor Sandon speaks of emotion-gratifying and
sensational views which, when the bubble is pricked—as inevitably it must be—may induce "a mood of cynicism from which
all scientific activity will suffer".[1] The geneticist Theodosius

[1] H. Sandon, *New Scientist*, 11 March 1966, p. 845.

Dobzansky reaches the same conclusion, arguing that it would be a fantastic coincidence if anything like man has emerged anywhere else in the entire universe and concludes, "I am inclined to wager that man is quite unique in the cosmos." [1,2]

Thus secular authorities are coming round to a position which Christians themselves have hardly dared, in recent times, to maintain. There is no doubt that the Christian revelation does *seem* to imply the uniqueness of man in the universe, even though it would be foolhardy to be dogmatic on the subject and even though over many centuries some Christians have taken a different view. In this connexion it is interesting to remind ourselves of the fact that many colonies of species (insects, plants, fish, seals, etc.) flourish in just *one* habitat and nowhere else in the whole world. In view of this it does not make scientific nonsense to think that man, so common here, is at this moment of cosmic time, likewise unique.

Developments of thought along the lines we have been considering are very different from what atheists expected. Indeed, the familiar argument that Christianity may be dismissed because God would not have sent His Son to die on just one of the countless billions of inhabited worlds is beginning to look less plausible than was once the case.

THE FLOOD

With regard to the flood, it now seems reasonably certain that a large area, which includes Mount Ararat, has been occasionally subjected to very extensive flooding in historic times.[3] These rare floods are not to be confused with normal but exaggerated flooding by rivers. After even the worst possible river flooding, a population returns a few months later when the floods subside—as still happens from time to time in China—and civilization in not disrupted.

[1] Dobzhansky, *Heredity and the Nature of Man*, 1965, p. 151.

[2] If man is a special creation by God then the arguments of Sandon, Dobzansky and others will not apply. There is no means of estimating the probability that God will act in a particular way.

[3] G. M. Lees and N. L. Falcon, *Geographical Journal*, 1952, **118**, 24; M. E. L. Mallowan, *Iraq*, 1964, **26**, 62; R. L. Raikes, *Iraq*, 1966, **28**, 52.

Up to 1952 it was supposed that the Persian Gulf had had a quiet geological history, with age-long silting up by the Tigris and Euphrates. Since then however, there have been finds of marine (fossil-bearing) sediments where river deposits were expected. Geologically there is upthrust in the mountain-range to the north, but subsidence, which seems to occur in sudden bursts, in the lowlands. This, coupled with silting by rivers and huge changes in sea level (variously computed—up to 300 feet) makes the geologically "recent" history of the area highly complex and no general picture is yet clear. It appears, however that land once extended far out to sea in the Persian Gulf and it is possible that some at least of the pre-flood cities are now covered by its waters.

A great flood occurred around 3000 B.C. but did not destroy the continuity of culture in the area. Noah's flood must have been much earlier and a date around 5000–7000 B.C. seems reasonable; the earlier date would make it coincide with the ending of the last Ice Age. Around this period there was vast flooding by the sea and for the first time the Black Sea became salt. Today extensive areas of desert around the Caspian Sea and in Iran are white with salt and marine shells are plentiful. Enclosed pockets of water have dried up or, like the Caspian Sea, are doing so. Before about 7000 B.C. the Plateau of Iran, now a desert, was inhabited—"most of it was rolling grassland, well-watered and providing a very desirable land and well fitted for human habitation".[1]

A well-established method of dating the past is to count the varves (periodic deposits of sand) formed by the retreating ice sheet after the last Ice Age, which melted rapidly in the summers and ceased melting in the winters. Here again the varves suggest that something unusual happened rather later than 7000 B.C.: varves of much greater than average thickness are found in Denmark, Norway and even in North America. This does not necessarily mean that the flood extended to all these regions, but it does seem to indicate some unusual happening in one single year in the distant past.

In view of the geological nature of the area, it is reasonable to suppose that Noah's flood, like one or two later floods, was

[1] Sir Arthur Keith, *A New Theory of Evolution*, 1948. See the very interesting discussion of these problems in P. O'Connell's *The Deluge and the Antiquity of Man* (Issued with *Science of Today and the Problems of Genesis*, 1959).

caused by a sudden widespread subsidence, followed possibly by partial rising of the land shortly afterwards. Another view is that, at the end of the Ice Age vast seas of melted ice were hemmed in behind ice barriers which, at a certain stage, suddenly gave way.

Yet another possibility is that the ice at the Antarctic was involved in some way. The southern ice sheet which (unlike the ice at the north) rests on a continental land mass, collects ice by precipitation at a rate which exceeds the rate of removal (by evaporation and formation of icebergs). According to a plausible and widely held theory, the ice sheet steadily thickens and increasing quantities of the world's supply of water become locked at the south. As the process continues, the pressure at the base of the ice increases and eventually the yield point of the ice is reached. When once movement starts friction at the base must cause melting, with the result that enormous quantities of ice slide rapidly into the ocean, raising the sea level throughout the world by at least 60–100 feet, and starting a new Ice Age by cooling the water and by reflecting the sun's light and heat back into space.[1]

If, as seems likely, this process happens rapidly, vast shock waves will cause catastrophic flooding of all save very high ground. It is believed that this process may repeat every 50–100,000 years, but as it last happened say around 40,000 years ago, it will not account for the Biblical flood. There are, however, indications in Antarctica that in places the ice was recently much thicker than at present, so that a large slip may well have taken place in historic times. If so, a gigantic tidal wave of water, coming up from the Southern hemisphere, may have engulfed early man.

So far much is guess-work. Indeed the widespread disbelief in

---

[1] The Southern ocean fills with floating ice which reflects more strongly than water. The lowered temperature reduces evaporation, removing cloud protection. Thus much of the sun's heat is lost to the earth. For further details see, for example, *Nature*, 1964, **201**, 147. Christians will think at once of God's conversation with Job; "Have you entered the storehouses of the snow, or have you seen the storehouses of the hail, which I have reserved for the time of trouble?" (*Job* 38: 22).

Grooving caused by ice has been seen on rocks exposed 450 metres above present ice level. It is thought that the reduction in Antarctic ice may have happened at the end of the last Ice Age, but dating is not yet satisfactory. T. Hatherington, (Ed), *Antarctica*, 1965, p. 245; J. A. Mercer, *Glaciological Notes* (IGY), 1962, II, 541.

the reality of Noah's flood has discouraged serious investigation: but the position is now changing. A helpful factor is the discovery of oil in the area, with the consequent encouragement of geological investigation.

Despite several expeditions, no trace of Noah's ark has been found on the Ararat range, but there would seem to be a possibility that it may one day be found. However the region is difficult and dangerous (owing the prevalence of smuggling) and usually the mountains are ice-covered.

Linking these facts with those which we discussed in the last chapter, we see that even on those topics in which it seemed to the Victorians that religion was in headlong retreat, the familiar pattern is emerging. Such developments as there have been would have proved most disconcerting to the Victorian sceptic and faith-confirming to the Christian. Today Christians may look forward to more future discoveries which will throw further light on man's beginnings and on the Noachian flood. The Christian may confidently expect that, in due time, all the outstanding problems will be solved and will confirm the Christian teaching on these subjects.

To summarize, despite setbacks in the Victorian era, it appears that science and Christianity are closely intertwined. Where scientific discoveries bear on questions of philosophy or religion, they fit in well with Christian belief. Conversely, the expectations of rationalists have often been contradicted by discoveries in the scientific world, or results have been of a surprising nature, difficult to reconcile with a rationalistic philosophy.

As we have noted from time to time, a few discoveries can reasonably be interpreted as exceptions to these findings—but on no showing can they be regarded as numerous. In view of lack of information and the ease with which mistakes can be made, a few exceptions are certainly to be expected: we have previously noted that no theory, scientific or otherwise, however valid it may be, can lead to *infallible* predictions as to the future course of discovery.

CHAPTER 18

CONCLUSION

ONE DIFFICULTY IN WRITING A BOOK OF THIS KIND is that it is hard to know when to stop! In one way and another the Bible is concerned with almost every field of learning—with a much wider range of topics, in fact, than it is possible for one mind to master—and the temptation is to read and write ever more and more and yet to feel that the horizon stretches farther and farther out into infinity! But a book must have an end! In this closing chapter we shall discuss a few further topics about which little or nothing has so far been said and, finally, we shall comment briefly about some of the principles which govern the study of the relationship of science to Christian faith.

PSYCHICAL RESEARCH

In Chapters 9, 10 and 11 we alluded briefly to psychical research in connexion both with the search for half-way substances, researches undertaken in Russia, and the Resurrection. However, a few more general comments seem desirable.

Christians have always held that telepathy is possible. Definite instances of its operation are recorded in the Bible[1] and the belief that God can show His will to a person who seeks it in prayer implies that a kind of telepathy can exist between man and God.[2] The same conclusion follows if we believe that God knows the secret thoughts of man. For the Christian, then, telepathy is a fact and as such ought to be discoverable by the methods of science. This does not guarantee the genuineness of any particular evidence —even if all the modern work on the subject were shown to be spurious, the Christian would still expect that one day telepathy would be verified.

[1] Especially 2 Kings 6: 8–12.
[2] W. E. Leslie, Trans. Victoria Institute, 1924, 56.

In contrast to this, sceptics, since the beginning of the modern era, have poured scorn on the possibility of telepathy, and in response to every claim of positive results have demanded a higher and ever-rising standard of evidence. It would be easy to cite many examples from their writings in this vein.

Today evidence for the existence of telepathy is so strong that it is reluctantly accepted even by many atheists. Although rearguard action has by no means ceased, mechanical "explanations" for the positive results obtained in laboratories in many lands are becoming increasingly implausible. We have noted (p. 83) that confirmation has been obtained even in Russia.

DEATH—THE END?

Another Christian belief, one common to most religions, is that there is continued existence after death. Though the subject, considered in the light of experimental science, is filled with pitfalls for the unwary, psychical researchers have accumulated a great mass of evidence which is more readily interpreted on this hypothesis than on any other.

There is no need, in this connexion, to adopt the spiritualistic hypothesis that the dead are communicating with the living—in fact, on this view, the evidence hitherto collected is quite difficult to explain at all. Nevertheless, there is certainly evidence that mediums *do* sometimes pick up information from dead people, information not known to the living, which has afterwards been verified. Probably the easiest interpretation of the facts is to suppose that the dreams or imaginations of the dead may sometimes be picked up telepathically—just as can the dreams of living people.

If we wish to argue that the dead are not in any way involved, then we must suppose that telepathy is delayed—thoughts which a person had while still alive being held in reserve, so to speak, and picked up several years after he is dead. However, this would still imply that thoughts continue to exist after death, and this again is contrary to what a materialist would expect.

Whatever the correct interpretation may be, the fact remains that many of the world's best intellects have worked on this problem over many years, and it is now impossible to dismiss—save on grounds of prejudice or wilful ignorance—the mass of positive evidence accumulated.

ARCHAEOLOGY—MEDICINE

Another important field of endeavour is that of archaeology. An older generation of sceptics regarded much of the historical portion of the Bible as legendary, denying the existence of many Old Testament characters such as Abraham, Isaac and Jacob. Archaeology, concerning which much has been written by competent scholars, has vindicated the historical accuracy of the Bible in many instances or has confirmed the general setting of the Biblical stories.

The same may be said of medical research. Many of the health laws of the Old Testament used to make no sense to the modern reader, because they seemed arbitrary and pointless. But as medical historians have often pointed out, they are usually (perhaps always) based on sound principles of hygiene. There are good reasons why, in hot countries, the pig should be regarded as an unclean animal and so not used for food; why blood should not be eaten; why hair should be shaved off in certain diseases; why refuse should be covered and so on.[1]

The atrocity stories of the Bible should also, probably, be viewed in this light. We are all familiar with the fact that an apparently good and respectable man may be apparently lacking in humanitarian principles in his relations with vermin or a human enemy. This rule certainly applied in the Old Testament.

Biologically, the failure of the conscience to function in certain directions may be connected with a genetical lack of protection against disease. To illustrate, a man who would be loth to kill an animal which did him no harm would feel no qualms about killing one which attacked human beings or harboured infectious diseases—compare most peoples' contrasting attitudes towards the squirrel and the rat.

An innate sense of a similar difference may be present in human societies: sometimes it may happen that only through one side

[1] See for example, C. F. V. Smout, *The Story of the History of Medicine*, 1964, Chapter 2; A. R. Short, *The Bible and Modern Medicine* (Paternoster Press), 1953.

winning in a war and completely wiping out the enemy, will it be possible for *either* side to live at all. We have already noted the effects of malaria, smallpox and other diseases on populations which are not genetically attuned to them (Chapter 7). We should probably look upon the atrocities of the Old Testament in this light. At a certain stage in the development of human societies when, owing to lack of transport and cultural contacts, they have been inbred and isolated over long periods, sudden fraterniza-tion would often lead to devastating destruction by disease. The Old Testament records a number of instances of sudden death which came simply because the Israelites fraternized and began to intermarry.[1] A Christian is not pledged to regard all these cruelties as expressions of the ultimate will of God, but he may begin to realize that conceivably they were sometimes necessary, even commanded, as the lesser of two evils.[2] Science is certainly making this viewpoint plausible and it removes much of the sting from the older atheistic arguments on the morality of the Bible.

BRAIN—A MACHINE

From another point of view, it is sometimes argued that medical science has made it more difficult to believe in religion. We are learning today that the brain is an instrument of fantastic com-plexity and that even small changes in its structure, or in the chemicals which the body manufactures for its use, can cause pro-found changes in the mind—moral character being changed by an operation on the brain or the administration of a drug. It is argued that man is not therefore a free agent and that, contrary to religious teaching, he cannot be held responsible for his actions. May there not even be substances in the blood of a criminal which makes him take to crime? Again, since the link between the brain and the mind is so close, why should we suppose that the latter continues to exist after the former has died?

[1] See J. R. Whitwell, *Syphilis in Earlier Times* (Lewis, London), 1940. Cf *Numbers* 25: 31, etc. Zimmerman, "Early Pathology of Syphilis, 1497–1563", *Janus*, 1934, **37**, 69; **38**, 1, shows how venereal disease, newly introduced, may kill within two or three days.

[2] Jesus spoke of a command given because of the hardness of mens' hearts (*Matthew* 19; 8). Had He lived today, might He not have spoken also of other commands given because of man's ignorance of the world around him?

These arguments, however, are less impressive than might appear. Modern developments, do not necessarily, *in principle*, raise new problems. Our ancestors believed that character was profoundly influenced by the positions of planets at the time of birth, by spleens, gall-bladders, etc., by bumps in heads or folds in the palm of the hand—or even by the spells of a witch. We must not suppose that new difficulties have been created because genes, new drugs and brain-washing have replaced the older influences.

It is interesting to note that some of these false scientific ideas of the past enjoyed the enthusiastic support of deists and atheists, at a time when Christians were rightly suspicious. Thus American freethought periodicals in the nineteenth century enthusiastically supported phrenology because it was considered that "if true it completely undermined the very foundations of Christianity".[1] Franz J. Gall, founder of phrenology, who lectured in Vienna, was stopped by the government in 1802 because his views seemed dangerous to religion. He visited prisons to find thieving bumps on prisoners' heads, and churches to look for "bumps of veneration"! (It is now said that the "locus of veneration", as located by Gall, is near the motor area connected with the movement of the big toe!) Farther back in the sixteenth century, we find enthusiastic support for astrology at a time when it seemed that Christianity was being undermined.[2]

The arguments of today differ little from those of yesterday and are no better supported. They are well in keeping with the tradition that rationalism supports views, however slender the evidence, if they show promise of undermining the Christian religion. The simple fact is that the brain is highly complicated and that we just do *not* know how it works. The fact that its proper working can be interfered with in many ways has been known for thousands of years and can be interpreted either in the way that the rationalist suggests, or else by supporting that, with its tool out of order, the mind can no longer make the physical body operate properly. Of the eminent

[1] A. Post, *Popular Freethought in America, 1825-50* (Columbia U.P.), 1943, p. 50. See also p. 229.

[2] D. C. Allen, *The Star-Crossed Renaissance* (Duke U.P.), 1941, Chapter 2.

neurophysiologists of today, perhaps half take one view and half the other.[1]

Moreover, the arguments we have been considering are two-edged. The more we learn to regard the brain as a fantastically complicated mechanism, the more fantastically difficult does it become to understand how such a complex mechanism could ever have come into existence at all. Compared with the complexity required the time available for the evolution of such a system seems very inadequate indeed, which lends colour to the view that the brain was planned in some way—a conclusion which no atheist will find palatable.

Another point worth making is that the Christian will see in these new developments a vindication of the Christian doctrine on judging. "Judge not that ye be not judged" is a principle that human beings have been slow to follow in the past. We are learning that the factors which influence people to do right or wrong are so complex that in the last resort no person is ever in a position to assess the amount of blame attaching to a wrongful act. Only God is the judge. The fact that genes, drugs and brain surgery influence character helps us to see good sense in this Christian doctrine.

PSYCHOLOGY

Much might be said about psychology. Here again, many of the new insights which have been discussed in recent years lie implicit at the heart of Christianity. It is commonly acknowledged that the understanding shown in the New Testament is profound: indeed it would probably be no exaggeration to say that few if any of the insights which are made use of by the modern therapist for the cure of sick minds cannot be traced back to this source. The New Testament accurately describes the inward war within the self, the difficulty of knowing one's own motives, the damaging effects of fear (in the sense of *dread*), the dangers of divided loyalty and many other points. Psychology of this kind, though of great value, is better regarded as an art than a science and this,

[1] The proportion holding views compatible with Christianity is now considerably larger than was the case a few decades back. See Preface in H. R. Smythies (Ed.) *Brain and Mind*, 1965.

coupled with the fact that there are many rival therapeutic psychologies, places it beyond the purview of this book.

INTERPRETATION

In discussing relatively minor points, the question of the interpretation of the Bible becomes increasingly important. Long before the days of modern science, Christians, basing their conclusions on the Bible alone, made interesting predictions as to the course of science and technology. Some suggested, for instance, that the time would come when it would be possible for man to travel to the ends of the earth in less than a day, or to see at distances of thousands of miles.[1] But though the interpretations may well be sound, they are not the common heritage of the Christian Church and will seem unconvincing to those accustomed to interpret the Bible in a different way.

Some prophecies, however, are less controversial. Many Christians (and most Mohammedans) think that Jesus will literally return at the second advent, when he will descend on the Mount of Olives. When this happens, "the mount of Olives shall cleave in the midst thereof toward the east and toward the west, and there shall be a very great valley; and half of the mountain shall remove toward the north, and half of it toward the south"[2] There are obvious geological implications here—if a large valley forms one day as a result of an earthquake, the rocks must be in tension. It is now known that the Jordan valley is in considerable tension and the formation of new valleys, and a continuation of the main valley northward, is not unlikely.[3] Geologically Arabia has been moving northwards since the Miocene, apparently rotating about a centre near the North of Egypt. As a result the Jordan valley is not only tending to widen, but is in a state of shear.[4] If, therefore,

---

[1] *Revelation* Chapter 11, as interpreted by the "Futurist" school of prophecy, suggests that people over the whole earth will know immediately of the death of two men in Jerusalem, that the dead bodies will be visible from remote places and that "VIP's" from great distances will have reached the city within a day or two.

[2] *Zechariah* 14: 4.

[3] R. W. Girdler, *Quart. Jour. Geol. Soc.*, 1958, **114**, 79

[4] See A. S. Laughton, *New Scientist*, 27 January 1966, p. 220, for a map of the area showing the geological features.

a mountain in the area were to be pulled apart in an earthquake by the East–West tension, we should expect its eastern half to move to the North, and the Western to the South.

This passage is remarkable too, on account of its prediction of a brilliant light which will confuse day and night—"And there shall be continuous day (it is known to the Lord), not day and not night, for at evening time there shall be light" (R.S.V.). We are reminded of earthquake lights, already discussed in Chapter 13. Detail of this kind is hard to explain unless we accept Biblical inspiration in some form.

AFTER-THE-EVENT INTERPRETATION

One difficulty is that we cannot always be certain how far popular proverbs, sayings and beliefs were incidentally made use of for the purpose of religious teaching. Just as today we speak of an ostrich-like behaviour without believing that, as a matter of natural history, ostriches put their heads in the sand to avoid being seen so, it may be, Jesus spoke of disciples being wise as serpents without implying that serpents are wise. Similarly the Psalmist's references to a many-headed dragon in the wilderness[1] doubtless refers to Egypt and not to an unknown biological species. We use similar expressions today (e.g. a two-faced person has not, anatomically speaking, two faces!) Given enough perversity or lack of knowledge it is possible to build a quite fantastic scientific picture from a collection of Biblical texts[2]—a foolish historian a thousand years hence might do the same for us on the basis of the language *we* use.

In this connexion we must not forget that Biblical exegesis and secular knowledge (which includes science) must always mutually interact upon one another. Biblical allusions to facts will be difficult to understand if we are ignorant of the facts referred to: quite often the meanings of words can be determined only by appeal to non-Biblical sources.

[1] *Psalm* 74: 14.
[2] As was done by Cosmas Indicopleustes in the sixth century. Cosmas's views had no enduring influence on Christian thought and were generally abandoned by the eighth century. His work is available in translation: J. W. McCrindle, *The Christian Topography of Cosmas an Egyptian Monk*, 1897.

There is danger, of course, in such an approach. If we reinterpret the Bible so as to bring it into line with science, we may destroy the evidence that agreement with science really exists. We must first be certain, then, that without such reinterpretation the agreement is there, certain that we are on the right track. But when the foundation is sure, it is safe to build.

We demand no special treatment for the Bible here. We treat all old documents in the same way. There is, for example, a passage in Aristotle's *Generation of Animals*[1] concerning lead ore which, we are told, increases in bulk and becomes thick, coherent and white when *pneuma* (spirit or air) gets into it. The passage was unintelligible to classical scholars, for no one had ever heard of black galena, or lead ore, behaving in so strange a way.

At the beginning of the present century the method of ore-dressing known as *flotation* was discovered and patented—first in connexion with gold-mining in Wales. In this the powdered mixture of ore and broken rock is mixed with water, a suitable oil is added, and air blown in. The ore alone then floats to the surface of the water, carried by bubbles. Even a black ore looks whitish in colour and is much increased in bulk. Today many millions of tons of ores are treated by this method every month throughout the world.

When Aristotle's description of the method used at an ancient lead mine was brought to his attention, Dr. P. J. Durrant, a chemist, at once recognized that it was a description of the flotation process. Undoubtedly, in at least one of their mines, the ancients had hit upon this valuable method for separating ore from unwanted material. In the same way, a man today, familiar with aspects of science and technology, may sometimes see the meaning of passages of Scripture which have been obscure for thousands of years.

CONCLUSION

To summarize our conclusions, the evidence shows that theology cannot be simply divorced from scientific discoveries. The

[1] Aristotle, *On the Generation of Animals,* Trans. A. L. Peck, 1943, p. 161.

Christian definitely has a stake in the results of the research laboratory. He may rightly claim that much modern scientific development concerns his belief, in the sense that results are such as he would expect if his faith were true. If, on rare occasions, and often for short periods in history only, it may seem to be otherwise in some isolated field of endeavour, there is no cause for alarm. No theory predicts all the right answers all the time. But considered as a whole, the Christian faith is surely remarkable in its predictive power even at the purely mundane scientific level. And this is a wonderful fact which can serve only to strengthen faith in those who view it reasonably.

We may conclude, then, that science has never been more favourable to Christian belief than today. Now in one connexion, now in another, discoveries are made, often unexpectedly, which fit in well with the expectations of the Christian believer. All told they are gratifyingly numerous, while those which seemingly point in the reverse direction are rare.

May we conclude from this that we can somehow "prove" Christianity? No. There can be no question of "proving" that Christianity—or for that matter any other belief—is true. The scientist can apply the words of Solomon to the whole edifice of scientific discovery—"Behold, heaven and the heaven of heavens cannot contain Thee; how much less this house that I have builded!"[1] All we discover is relatively trivial and cannot measure up to the vast ultimate of God and His universe.

But though this is true, it is no reason for divorcing science and religion. Knowledge is gained by suggesting a theory and then finding out as best one may whether the facts are in agreement, but a theory always goes *beyond* the facts. Within our experience hydrogen and oxygen combine to give water, but we cannot prove that this will always be true for all specimens of the elements throughout the universe: we find a law of gravity here on earth and in the solar system, but cannot prove that it will apply in distant parts of the skies. Theories apply far beyond our experiments and observations. We can never prove that they are *universally* true, only that in the limited fields where we try them out the facts agree with what we may expect on the basis of their truth. There is always an

[1] 1 *Kings* 8: 27.

element of faith—of belief, held without evidence—that laws apply in realms beyond our observations.

It is so with Christianity. We cannot "prove" it true. But we can say, "If it is true, we may expect this or that to follow." And when it does follow—not once only but again and again—faith is strengthened and confirmed.

INDEX

(*Subjects are in Italics*)